DETROIT MADAM

My Girls, My Rules, My Night

AYANNA WILLIAMS-JONES

DETROIT MADAM

Print ISBN: 9781736279625
Ebook ISBN: 9781736279601
Hardcover ISBN: 9781736279618

Detroit Madam is based on true events. Names, characters, some locations, and some incidents have been changed to protect privacy.

Acknowledgements/Dedications

Writing a book is harder than I thought and more rewarding than I could have ever imagined. Everything I do and have done in my life has been for my children to have a better life.

My dedication goes to my oldest son Jamier Williams who has taught me so many things in life. Your death has pushed me to go harder than I ever have before and even though I know you are in a better place I wish you were here with me and will never forget you until we meet again. I love you with all my heart Sincere Jam.

To my family:

Jayanna Williams my mini me and Nurse. Jamier has transferred the torch to you to overlook your sisters and brother and to look out for them. Just know if you need to smack them, he will be right there with you for emotional and mental support.

Amajenee Smith my Psychologist. Being the middle child isn't easy, but somebody has to do it and what better person than you. We don't always agree but know I have your back always and forever.

Carlos Smith my Esquire. My baby boy that isn't a baby anymore. I so look forward to seeing you in the court room killing the competition and taking your law firm to the next level.

Brooklyn Jones the Pediatrician. Named after my hometown you have that Brooklyn and Detroit in you so you are destined to be whoever and whatever you want to be.

DETROIT MADAM

Timothy Lewis my Husband. We have been inseparable from our first date. You have backed me and supported me with no questions asked even when you didn't know what my plans were. I look forward to spending the rest of my life with you.

Deborah Williams my Mother. I look forward to reading your book soon. Thank you so much for the hard love that made me into the woman I have become.

Finally, to all those who have been a part of my getting there: Kendra Patterson, Robert Patterson Jr, Nikki Curl, Venus Brown-Williams, Odessa Matthews, Latonya Richardson and Ramon Calvin.

To the original Boss Ladies team who have mentored and impacted my life: Shamika McKinley, Vinnie Potestivo, Big Machine Agency, Nya Marshall, Gail McMiddleton, Terry Tidwell, Julie Day, Margaret Stevenson, Dr. Rhonda Turpin and Cheryl Adams.

To my ghostwriters and editors for making this possible: Derek Nesbitt, Felice Laverne and Brenda Hampton

Chapter One

At sixteen years old, my life changed forever. It all started at IHOP in 1994, when I was a runaway working under a fake ID—the very definition of being grown before my years. I was waitressing that day, and the second I picked up a hefty tip from the table, I looked up and locked eyes with one of the finest, light-skinned niggas I had ever seen. He had a five-foot, eleven-inch muscular frame that was sculptured to perfection. As he headed my way, I could barely move. My feet felt like bricks and beads of sweat started to dot my forehead. The closer he got to me, the more I wanted to scream. Instead, I sucked in a deep breath, trying to calm myself.

"Yo. Can a brotha get somethin' to eat?" he asked.

Without waiting for a response, he sat arrogantly at the booth and picked up a menu. I nervously removed a pen and pad from the blue apron that was tied around my waist and gazed at him with a pleasant smile.

"Tell me what you want and I can get that for you," I said.

His eyes traveled from my firm breasts to the tips of my clean white tennis shoes. I was so mesmerized by his thick lips that defined sexy. When he swiped his tongue across his bottom lip, I felt my heart thump hard against my chest. My young mind could only take so much; he was the kind of man I had dreamed about.

"What's your name and where you from, brown sugga?" he asked.

Surprised by his question, I widened my eyes and stuttered. "I, uh, my name is Kandi. I'm from Bed-Stuy, Brooklyn, New York, but I was raised in Detroit. Why you asking, and what's yo name?"

Ignoring my questions, he slowly nodded while glancing at the menu again. As he was occupied with the menu, it gave me more time to examine how fine he was. I predicted he was somewhere in his late twenties. His skin appeared silky smooth, hair flowed with coal black waves, and there was something mysterious behind the shape of his hooded eyes. There was no way in hell he was interested in a youngin like me, but after that day, he continued to come back to IHOP, sit in my section and chat with me. His name was Dominic. Dominic . . . a real muthafucking hustler. I loved every bit of his persona, and the more I saw him, we started to click. I found out he was almost ten years my senior, but in no way did that matter to me. It wasn't long before he asked me to join him on a double date. I was head over heels about spending more time with him. He loved my go-getter personality and appreciated that I lived in Detroit. Detroit was in my blood—in my bones. Having Detroit and New York in me, I had to be a boss; he recognized it right away. I would soon discover how what was in my blood worked to my benefit.

On the day of my double date with Dominic, I grabbed my best friend, Dallas, who I'd been kicking it with ever since I was thirteen. We rigged up a lie to tell my Aunt Princess who I was living with at the time, instead of with my mother. She and I weren't getting along well. I couldn't deal with her strict ways, so I ran away and wound up staying with my aunt. She lived in a black, working-class neighborhood. Dallas, who was twelve, lived directly across the street from her and that shit was like fate. The minute we linked, shit kicked off and we'd been hanging like wet clothes ever since. I was the short, dark-skinned loud one, and she was the tall, lighter-skinned quiet one with an East Detroit, rough-around-the-edges kind of look. She always acted so much older than me because of the hard life she'd had while growing up. We were like two peas in a pod, and without saying a word to anyone, most people knew I was spending the night at Dallas' house or she would be at mine. That particular night, I told my Aunt Princess I would be at Dallas' house. Instead, Dominic and one of his boys, Trey, picked us up and drove us to a small apartment on the other side of Detroit. The apartment was cramped as fuck on the inside and the walls were a dingy white. I hadn't a clue whose place it was, but there was a potent smell of marijuana that permeated the air. Dallas and I sat on a plaid covered sofa giggling, chit-chatting and bobbing our heads to Dr. Dre's latest joint. We could hear Dominic and Trey arguing about something in the kitchen. Afraid that something might pop off, Dallas leaned closer to me and whispered.

"What them niggas in there arguing about? Maybe we should hurry up and get the fuck outta here," she suggested.

I shrugged my shoulders and tuned out the music thumping in the background. "I'm not sure what's up, but shit getting kind of heated."

Just then, Trey appeared in the kitchen's doorway with a frown on his face. His beady eyes shifted from me to Dallas.

"Aye, I'mma need y'all to make a move and go back home. Something came up. We need to do this date thing some other time," he said.

Dallas and I looked at each other with curiosity in our eyes. She cocked her head back, while lashing out at him with much attitude.

"That's fine, but either you or Dominic need to take us back home. I know you don't expect us to walk, do you?"

Trey sucked his teeth while lighting a blunt. "I was expecting to get some pussy and since you ain't putting out, walking is the only way you gon' get home."

Dallas shot up from the sofa. Displaying much anger, she darted her finger at him. "Muthafucka, are you a fool or a damn fool? We ain't walking no damn where, but you know what?" She snatched up her purse from the sofa and tucked it underneath her arm. "Never mind, girl, let's go. These niggas trippin'. I know *my* fucking way home. I don't mind walking. It'll give me a minute to cool the hell off!"

Hell, I was a suburban girl who didn't know how to get back to the other side of town, especially in the middle of the damn night.

"I know you mad," I said, folding my arms across my chest. "But if these niggas brought us here, they need to take us home."

I rolled my eyes at Trey and Dominic who was now standing next to him. Dominic appeared calm as ever. He nudged his head towards the door.

"Silence the noise," he said. "I'll take y'all home. Go get in the car."

Sighing from relief, me and Dallas rushed to leave the apartment and got in the car. Dominic got in, but during the whole ride to my house, he never said one word. I wasn't sure what the argument between him and Trey was about, but at that point, it didn't even matter. I was just glad to be on my way home to see my auntie again. She was the type of person who didn't play no games. I liked living with her, because she showed me respect and didn't fuss at me all the time. We avoided arguments. That was a plus for a teenager like me who didn't always like to follow strict rules. One of her pet peeves was when folks pulled up in her driveway and honked the horn, instead of coming to the door. Anytime someone would pull up in the driveway for me and honk the horn, she wouldn't allow me to peek out the window or open the door. All she would say to them was, "Don't no hoes live here." Then she'd tell me, "Tell them to come to the door and ask for you."

I didn't want her to know where I'd been that night, so I told Dominic to pull over at the corner of our block. He parked near the curb, and as soon as my hand touched the doorknob, that's when I heard his masculine voice.

"Be good, brown sugga. And I'll see you when I see you, au'ight?"

I swallowed the lump in my throat, figuring this was goodbye for now. All I did was nod my head, and after exiting the car, Dallas and I stood on the corner. We watched Dominic speed away. Knowing that my aunt would trip, he purposely drove past my house and honked the damn horn. Just so my auntie wouldn't know the honking had anything to do with me, Dallas and I walked the whole block before going into the house. And when we did, I stayed up the whole night wondering when I would ever see Dominic again. Unfortunately for me, he never came back to IHOP again.

***

At the age of eighteen, I ran into Dominic again. I had just had my first son and was walking down the street with him in a stroller. By then, I'd moved back home to Oak Park, a northern suburb of Detroit, to live with my mom. We had settled some of our differences, and she'd reached out to help me with my son. I was grateful, but seeing Dominic again changed my life forever. It set me on a path I didn't even know I'd be following. With a pink jogging suit on and my hair slicked back into a ponytail, I halted my steps and looked into the car as he pulled closer to the curb. Seeing how fine he was put an instant smile on my face. There was something about the way he licked across his lips that sent me in a trance.

"Aye, don't I know you from somewhere?" he asked.

"I know you would never forget this pretty face, but I'm Kandi. The one who used to work at IHOP."

He snapped his fingers and flashed his pearly white teeth. "That's right. I can never forget a pretty face like yours. Where you going, brown sugga?"

He glanced at my son who was sound asleep. A binky was still in his mouth and he was wrapped tight in a warm blue blanket.

"I'm on my way home. Just went for a walk to clear my head, and I live about three blocks down the street."

Dominic reached over and pushed the door open. "Get in. I'll take you home. You have my word that I won't leave you hanging again."

I blushed and shook my head. "Oh, so you do remember me. That's good cause I still remember you, too."

Without saying another word, I got in the car with my son. Dominic drove me home that day, and after dating him for less than six months, my son and I had moved in with him on the east side of Detroit, near the airport.

The way I saw it, we were living a new and improved lavish lifestyle. I'd gone from being a child at home doing chores and rushing to get in before my curfew, to being a kept woman whose sole job was taking care of my son. Dominic took real good care of us. He didn't require much from me at all; I didn't even have to do laundry. We just dropped that shit off every week and had it done for us. Life was good, and since I'd had my own place now, the least I could do was whip up home-cooked meals for my man. He appreciated my efforts, and even though my cooking was mediocre, he never criticized me for trying.

"What's this?" he asked with his head cocked back, examining the food on a fork. I sat on his lap while trying to feed him mac and cheese I'd just made.

"What does it look like?" I replied, laughing.

"I ain't sure, but I'm more concerned about what it tastes like."

"Well, open yo mouth and see."

He opened his mouth, and as I fed him mac and cheese, he chewed, nodded and then laughed. "I still don't know what it is, but you hooked that shit up, girl. Now all I need is something real sweet to make me feel high."

One of my main priorities was doing whatever I could to make my man feel high. I knew exactly what he needed, so I leaned in and planted passionate kisses on those thick lips of his I loved dearly. His strong hands eased underneath my navy silk robe and roamed my curvaceous ass. But right after I positioned myself to straddle his lap, I heard my son call for me. Dominic lightly patted my ass, then backed away from our kiss.

"Go see about him," he said, then winked. "You can take care of me later."

Intending to do just that, I smiled and tightened the belt on my robe. I left the kitchen, thinking about how Dominic was one of the best things that had ever happened to me. He took care of us more than we took care of him. He had been married before, but because his ex-wife wouldn't let him see his daughter on a regular basis, he bonded with my son immediately. They adored each other. There was a time, though, when Dominic made it clear to my son's father that he didn't have a kid in our house and he didn't want him to call my son anymore. I was pissed because how in the fuck could my son's father let another nigga tell him some shit like that and go along with it? He did as he was told and barely came around after that. I started to realize that Dominic's controlling ways had more power than I'd thought. I admired his ability to control his surroundings, and being a hustler attracted me to him even more, but the control issues would later be the death of us. He was well known around the city of Detroit as a graphic designer. No petty designer either—he hustled hard. His unique work spoke volumes. He designed different images on clothing, shoes, jackets . . . and even created backdrops for some of the hottest names in the game during that time. Artists like LL Cool J, Salt-N-Pepa, Teddy Riley, John Sally . . . they all came to Dominic. He'd designed the robe LL Cool J wore in the "Mama Said Knock You Out" video, and at one point, he used to date Salt-N-Pepa's Pepa. His reputation with the elite crowd made him a street celeb in town. I didn't know his status, until we'd started dating. He'd never mentioned it to me before then.

Not only did Dominic work with major rap artists, but one of the biggest artists he had hoped to work with was Prince. Dominic would design jackets and backdrops with Prince's face or image, and the whole entire city would go crazy over the designs he'd put together. Whenever Prince had concerts in Detroit or was there on business, Dominic would show up to display his talents. Prince took notice, but would never approach Dominic or say anything about his work. Later on down the road, Dominic's aggressive approach worked against him, especially when it was his time to shine.

Meanwhile, Dominic was invited to every single celeb party and event that came through Detroit. We had access to concerts and VIP areas backstage. Many times, he designed jackets the celebs wore on stage. Those moments were the highlights of his life. And there I was, at eighteen years old, right beside him and dating the man of my dreams. He had hella swag and was one of the hottest niggas in the city at the time. No doubt, I was riding high, but I wasn't used to all the glam, rubbing shoulders with celebrities or having VIP access to events. This type of shit was what I'd seen on TV, but there I was in the midst of it all, feeling on top of the world. Everything was fucking great, and Dominic was stacking paper like crazy. He had opened doors for me and had introduced me, and my friends, to a new lifestyle he had been living in for quite a while.

"This is how a woman should dress," he said as we stood in an expensive clothing store. "I want you to start rockin' shit like this and I'm taking you to get your hair done later. I saw this fly-ass style I want you to wear."

18

A part of me was hyped about him buying me clothes and showing me how he wanted me to style my hair, but I also felt embarrassed. I questioned if I was good enough for him, and after he saw the disappointment in my eyes, he lifted my chin up with his finger.

"What's wrong?" he asked. "Don't you like this outfit?"

I slowly nodded and removed the sexy two-piece pantsuit from his hands. "I love it. You just do so much shit for me, and—"

Dominic silenced me with a wet kiss that calmed any concerns I'd had. Bottom line, he made me feel loved. He was like a new daddy to me. I felt like a sponge that was absorbing a whole new way of life and style from him. I'd had some street knowledge, mostly learned from my own daddy who was a hustler. But the knowledge he taught me was nothing that could compare to what I'd learned from Dominic. He was schooling me. If he walked around in brand-named clothing dripped with gold chains, diamonds and flashy jewelry, I had to do the same. If his haircut was sharply lined and waves flowed every single week, my shit had to be right, too. I couldn't look like a bum-ass bitch beside a nigga like him, and I became more than impressed by the transformation he'd suggested.

In addition to my appearance, he sharpened my street smarts and awakened me to the crazy ass world we lived in. That day, we were on our way to a nightclub and were riding in the back of a black stretch limousine. I rocked a gold metallic dress that melted on my curves. It had a plunging neckline that revealed my cleavage and a diamond necklace draped between them. My feathered hair was swooped to one side, and the gold hoop earrings and high-heeled black pumps I wore made me look like a million bucks. Dominic looked fine as fuck in a black Adidas sweat suit and tennis shoes. His facial hair was neatly trimmed, bling was sparkling and sandalwood smelling cologne had the crotch of my panties wet. He faced me and recited the rules.

"Don't be out there partying with yo girls and leave yo drink around. Somebody might slip something in that shit when you ain't looking. Got it?"

I nodded while absorbing more wisdom from him. My girls and I were a bit on the wild side at times, and some men looked for opportunities to do slick shit like that and take advantage of us. Dominic was always ten steps ahead of the game. He did his best to make sure I was up on mine as well. After paying me a compliment, he reached over and squeezed my hand with his. Then he reminded me what would take place, after the party was over.

"We should check out of this joint no later than two or three in the morning. After we leave, I need you to do something for me."

I had a feeling what he was talking about, but decided to play clueless. "What's that?" I asked. "You know I'll do anything for you, right?"

I smiled, hoping his request would be *simple*. Instead, he hit me with some shit that had come up months ago about swinging.

"I need you to invite Patrice and James to our crib so we can do some things. You said you would do it, remember?"

Hell, yeah, I remembered, but I forced myself not to talk about it. "Things like what?" I asked. "Patrice said they were coming over to the house, but not until tomorrow."

Dominic seemed irritated and shrugged his shoulders. "Today, tomorrow, whenever. Just make sure they come so we can do some of the shit I like to do to you."

My face twisted, and a knot in my stomach started to tighten. "I'm confused. I know what you like to do to me, and you know what I like to do to you. What does that have to do with Patrice and James?"

A sly smirk appeared on his face. Dominic was blunt, but it wasn't the first time he'd talked about swinging. "I want us to swing with another couple. Maybe I'll just watch while you have sex with them. It depends on what kind of mood I'm in."

I playfully pushed his shoulder, hoping he would rethink this shit. "Whatever, man. Stop talking that shit. Ain't nobody got time for that."

He stared at me without a single blink. Seriousness was in his eyes; I knew when Dominic wasn't playing. The smile on my face quickly vanished. I swallowed a huge lump in my throat, and the knot in my stomach had tightened even more. My voice, however, remained calm.

"All I wanna know is how can you love me and want me to have sex with another man? How can you want to have sex with another woman? That's bullshit, man. We can't do no shit like that."

"It's just sex, baby. And the last time I checked, having sex ain't never hurt nobody. If you haven't tried it, how can you knock it? I think it'll be fun, and trust me when I say that you gon' like that shit, too."

With tears at the rim of my eyes, I turned my head and gazed out of the window. I reminisced about an incident that had happened when I'd lived with my mother. I had just started to date Dominic. He'd mentioned this swinging shit to me, but it went way over my head.

That particular day, I was at my mama's house. I couldn't reach Dominic, and my ass kept calling him over and over again. He wouldn't pick up the phone, and the more he ignored me, I got anxious. I slammed the phone down then called Dallas for backup and support.

"Girl, this muthafucka ain't answering his phone. Put some clothes on and ride to his crib with me. Something is up. I need to find out what the fuck is going on."

"I'll go with you, but what about the baby? You think yo Mama will watch him? And what if that nigga over there fucking another bitch? What you gon' do, beat his ass?"

"You damn right I am. And her ass too! I'm taking my baby with me. I can't ask my Mama nothing, and you know I gotta steal her damn car to get there."

"Bitch, you tripping. But I'ma go with you just in case we gotta fuck that nigga up. I hope he ain't wasting yo damn time. If he is, he about to pay for it."

Getting madder by the minute, I slammed the phone down and rushed to leave with my son. It was past midnight, so my mama was sound asleep when I quietly tiptoed in her bedroom, swiped the keys from her dresser and slipped them into my pocket. It was the first and only time I ever stole her car, but I was eager to get to Dominic. Like a bat out of hell, I picked up Dallas and drove my mom's Thunderbird all the way to the east side of Detroit. I swerved the car in his driveway and marched straight to the front door with anger all over my face. With tightened fists, I banged on the door so hard that the windows shook. A few minutes later, Dominic appeared on the balcony above me. I looked up to find him butt-ass naked with his chest on swole. Of course he didn't think it was me banging at his door because I didn't have a car.

"Who the fuck is it?" he yelled. He looked down and could barely see me because it was dark. I saw him squinting; he finally realized it was me. "What the fuck you doing here? And how'd you even get here?"

"I got my mama's car!" I yelled with my hand on my hip. "Why the hell you ain't answering the phone?"

I heard voices and much laughter coming from the inside of his house. He wasn't alone, and if he didn't have any clothes on, I was sure no one else did.

Minutes later, he came downstairs and tried to explain what was transpiring. And as I stood with my emotions running high, he hugged me with a cotton robe on. The belt was tightened around his waist, and the smell of sex was seeping through his pores.

"I wanna be with you," he said. "But you don't do this. You don't swing, and that's what I like to do. My ex like to do it, too, but you—"

I shoved him back, but whatever his ex was willing to do for him, I felt like I needed to do it as well. "I don't want you to do that with her, so I'll do it too! Now tell whoever is in there with you to leave. We'll talk about this later!"

For the time being, this incident was squashed. The only problem I had now was getting back home without my mama finding out I'd stolen her car. In deep thought about what had occurred at Dominic's place, I whipped across town to drop Dallas off. I then drove home and saw that someone had taken the previous parking spot where my mama's car was parked. She always parked in the same parking spot in front of her place. I was fucked because there wasn't a chance in hell she wouldn't notice her car had moved. But with my baby in my arms, I crept back inside and hoped that the Lord heard my prayers about her not knowing I was gone. Thankfully, she never said one word. That was the first time I'd gotten away with being so slick, and it was also the first time Dominic had introduced me to his new world. I avoided it that day, but I knew that once I moved in with him,

I'd have to do exactly what I promised to do.

As I remained quiet in the limousine, Dominic could tell I was uneasy about his request. And after that day, I continued to renege on what I'd promised and kept telling him I couldn't go through with it. He revealed to me that he had always been heavy into swinging. I was so uncomfortable with the shit, and it made me doubt his true love for me. As he opened up more to me about his past experiences that had happened when he was much younger, I was shocked as hell. He had been introduced to swinging at a very young age and operated more as a voyeur who often stood back and just watched people have sex. On many occasions, he'd watched his drug addicted mama as she tricked niggas for drug money. Now, as a man, he was still getting turned on by watching people fuck. He even admitted to hiding in closets while watching people. It appeared that he was stuck in an endless cycle from a past that haunted him every single day.

"Do it for me," he said, as we lay in bed talking that day. "Just one time, and if you don't like the shit, you don't have to do it again."

While biting my nails, I was so reluctant to respond. A huge part of me wanted to stand my ground and say no, but he had done so much for me. How could I not do this for him? It was the least I could do, and if I didn't like it, I could just walk away, *right?* There was a true tug-of-war happening in my mind, but when all was said and done, I agreed to go through with it. Dominic was thrilled. He reached over to hug me, and he reminded me, once again, how much he loved me.

"Don't ever doubt how I feel about you. Deep in yo heart, you already know what we got in this relationship is bigger than just sex."

Of course I had doubts, but my heart wouldn't allow me to tell the man who meant so much to me no. Like it or not, it was game on.

Chapter Two

Dominic had been so right about swinging. After the first time, swinging turned into a vital part of my lifestyle, even more than it did his. He remained more of a voyeur than an active participant, and this lifestyle was the beginning of me being classified as the Detroit Madam. At the time, I certainly didn't know what any of this would lead to. But neither of us wanted to depart from it. I surely didn't want to because swinging became a norm. It was something I had to do my way or not do it at all. See, even at that young age, I had become serious about my money. I knew it wasn't beneficial to just swing for the hell of it, and I wasn't about to give no nigga what he wanted, without getting what I wanted in return. So, I decided to make a business out of it. My motto has always been *if it makes money then it makes sense.* So, in order for a man to get what he wanted from me— Dominic to watch me having sex with some random man I'd never even met before—I needed to get paid for that shit. My first business started from that very idea. We'd throw parties—not just swinger's parties, but parties that hood niggas in the D would actually want to come to. In the hood environment back in the 90's, those kinds of parties weren't cool and niggas weren't typically into that voyeuristic swinger shit. Men weren't into letting another nigga watch them have sex, so we discussed and discovered ways to add it to the mix and make everybody happy. That simply meant having parties that resembled strip clubs. Girls in sexy dance outfits would shake their asses at these parties for tips. I'd charge money at the door, and then I'd find a man I was attracted to at the party and wanted to fuck. I'd make him feel lucky, like he was the only man in the room who had garnered my attention. Then I'd take him to the back room where Dominic would already be waiting as a voyeur in the closet to watch us. At the end of the night, he counted up all the money. Not only was I getting good dick and turning my man on, but I was getting paid to do it at the same time. That made sense in my world, and I was now doing everything I could to make my man happy, vice versa. Dominic knew I loved light-skinned pretty niggas, just like him. To show he was still in control, he often chose the guy I'd have sex with. His choices were always the opposite of him, which were darker-skinned mandingos—the kind of men I was less likely to cheat on with behind his back. He wanted them to look like they'd just gotten off a slave ship, truth be told. But I preferred to pick my own partners and not have to deal with his damn insecurities. That meant, some nights, it was difficult for me to find a guy to sleep with because the selection wasn't to my taste. If they weren't, my performance wasn't up to par, and sex was a wrap within five minutes. The bottom line was I needed a muthafucka with swag, like on some type of Blair Underwood shit. Those types of niggas energized me, and if Dominic wanted to see the best in me, he knew he had to step it up with his choices. Needless to say, he did and our empire grew. Our new business name was Sweet Sensation, which was named after me, Dallas, who went by "Honey" and my voluptuous friend, Cherry.

Dallas was down for the cause, but at the time, she was dating a prominent biker in a biker gang. Due to who he was, he didn't like the idea of her having sex with other niggas. So, for a while, she just worked the door and kept a lookout on the perimeter of the place in case of trouble. Her position didn't last for long because she'd gotten so many propositions from men who were willing to pay her for dancing. She was very attractive, and her caramel colored skin, light brown eyes and well-endowed breasts were assets to our movement. We talked about her next move while standing on the porch that day. Rap music was thumping loudly inside, and while some niggas were in there shooting craps, others were waiting for the dancing to start.

"I don't know what the fuck to do," Dallas said while watching two men in a car park across the street. "Kenny gon' kill me if I do this shit. But these niggas ready to see my thong and stuff that bitch with dollars. I'm fucking torn. What should I do?"

"You should do what yo gut is telling you to do," Cherry advised. "That is, go in there, shake that ass, get yo paper and tell Kenny fuck him. You gotta keep some money in yo pockets, too."

"I know that's right," I said. "Besides, what he don't know won't hurt him, and the last time I checked, this shit ain't got nothing to do with feelings. Get yo money, girl. All of it and send these niggas home with smiles on their faces."

We laughed, and after thinking about her decision for a few more minutes, Dallas jiggled her ass and slapped it. "Fuck it! I'ma 'bout to go make me some money, so step the hell aside cause here I come."

We high-fived each other, and from then on, Dallas was dancing right alongside me and Cherry. We'd gotten some skimpy new dancing outfits that barely covered our titties and coochies. Asses were visible for every eye to see, and with high heels on, we strutted around plenty of parties, owning that shit. More men came, as did more money. And soon enough, we recruited other girls to join us. They were eager to make money, and in an effort to get more niggas to show up, I advertised the parties as events being put on by me and my girls. The focus was always on us, that way the niggas we fucked with didn't get suspicious and think it was a trap to rob them. We had to be real careful and we made sure the men who paid for our services felt safe and welcomed. Even while Dallas and I passed out flyers to our events, we flirted with men, teased the hell out of them and made them feel *special*.

"Be sure to stop by the party this weekend to see what's up," I said, handing out flyers to a group of men at a carwash. Dallas and I wore bikinis while flaunting our flawless bodies. Every single eye at the carwash was on us; we had the men drooling.

"Daaaamn," one man said, grabbing his crotch. "Why we gotta come to the party to see what's up? Show a nigga what's up now?"

I aggressively stepped up to the man and pressed my breasts against his chest. I could feel his dick brick up, and that's when I reached down to touch it. "I said this weekend. All you gotta do is look for me. I can guarantee you a night you ain't gon' never forget."

I rubbed my hand on his package, before backing away from him. As sweat formed on the nigga's forehead, he wiped across it. The other men circled us. They seemed real hyped about showing up.

"I will be there!" Another nigga yelled. "Especially if y'all wearing those bikinis."

"Baby, if you like our bikinis, then you definitely gon' like my ruby red thong," Dallas teased. "And if you think we cute, wait 'til you see the other girls!"

The man rubbed his hands together, while smiling with glee in his eyes. Just like the others, he seemed anxious for the weekend to arrive. When it did, that party was the best one yet. We bumped up the fee to get in at the door, and the place was so packed that niggas could barely move around. They did, however, make room for my girls and me to do our thing. Money was dropping everywhere, and as soon as I set my eyes on a light-skinned tenderoni with a trimmed, short afro, I made my move to take him to the bedroom and fuck. Dominic was already in the closet ready to watch. I figured he would be pissed about my choice for that night. There were times when I played by my own rules, and that particular night, I just couldn't let a sexy nigga like Mr. Tenderoni go to waste.

Tipsy from drinking, Mr. T damn near busted down the door as we made our way into the back room that had a queen-sized bed up against the wall. The whole room was dimly lit and the window was covered with shiny gold curtains to jazz up the space. Light music thumped in the background, and the bed was covered in black silk sheets. For comfort, plush pillows were propped everywhere. We wanted the men to encounter memorable experiences, that way they'd keep coming back for more. With my dance clothes already ripped off, I eased back on the edge of the bed and slowly parted my legs. Doing the norm, my eyes shifted to the closet where Dominic was. I could always see his beady eyes peeking through the crack. Sometimes I'd wink at him, but that night I decided to keep my attention focused on the fine-ass piece of specimen in front of me. I watched as he quickly dropped his jeans and boxers to his ankles. He stepped out of them, and his massive dick rose to the occasion. I was so eager to feel it inside of me, but when I reached out to grab it, he stumbled forward, falling over me.

"Hold up, lil mama," he said. "Let me get a taste of that pussy, before I hammer it."

I was all for him tasting me, so I released his steel and kept my eyes locked on his as he dropped to his knees. He threw my legs over his broad shoulders, and seconds later, his tongue entered my creamy

insides like a slithering snake. I jerked back, unable to control my

shaky thighs that trembled out of control. The twirling of his slippery

tongue made me hum more than usual, and there were times I had to

fake that shit just so Dominic would get turned on. This time, I hadn't

faked a damn thing. This nigga had skills, but unfortunately, it was

only with his mouth. His dick didn't come through for me. After three

or four long strokes, it was a wrap. I was so mad that I pounded my fist

on the bed and grunted while he lay on top of me taking deep breaths.

"What's wrong with you?" he asked. "You alright?"

I rolled my eyes and pushed his shoulder back so he'd get off

me. He was sweating profusely—his skin was sticking to mine.

"I'm fine, but yo body is heavy," I said. "Move back."

I didn't want to insult him; after all, I still had to get paid. But

he damn well knew what was wrong with me. His dick wasn't about

shit, but at least he had a tongue that gave me some of the satisfaction I

needed. The rest came when he slapped money in my hand. I tightened

my hand to squeeze it, then my eyes shifted to the closet again. This

time, I winked at Dominic.

After the man left the room, I went into the bathroom to clean myself up. While I was in there, Dominic opened the door and came inside. He folded his arms across his chest while stroking the fine hair on his chin.

"That's what you get," he said, laughing. "I told you about fucking with those types of niggas, didn't I?"

I pursed my lips while wiping my slit with a warm towel. "I've definitely had better. And you know much better than I do that what looks good on the outside might not always feel good on the inside."

"Lesson number one, stick to the plan and you won't ever get disappointed."

I placed the towel on the sink, then reached for the money that was tucked in my top. I gave the money to Dominic. "Lesson number two," I said as a rebuttal. "At least we got paid."

Hell, we all got paid. Business was thriving even better than any of us had ever imagined. Mainly because we didn't have the usual come-up story, when it came to this lifestyle, where things started off slow then eventually picked up. Shit instantly took off, especially when the word touched down. Our hard work paid off, and we would

37

go to all the popping after-hour joints on the other side of town to meet people, network and invite them to our events. It was hard to classify us as just freaky-ass hustlers, because we were very smart about every single move we made. If marketing and branding was a thing at the time, we invented the shit. Just to make sure everything was set up right, we went downtown and applied for a DBA (doing business as) license, which let us use a business name without creating a formal legal entity such as a corporation or LLC. We also had business cards made. Advertising ended up being our boots on the ground—our bikinis on the ground was more like it. We strolled downtown in thong bikinis and even paraded our curvaceous bodies on the beach, while passing out business cards. Some people didn't like to see sexy young women, especially black women, being so free and open about our business. The way I saw it, we were on a mission. I didn't give a damn about what other people thought, and as a white woman on the beach tried to shame us, Dallas stopped to put that bitch in her place.

"What the hell are you doing out here?" the bony-ass woman yelled while shielding her husband's eyes as he sat there lusting. "There are kids out here!"

"You need to be more concerned about yo husband," Dallas said. "And if you don't mind yo own damn business, I'ma pull him into that Johnny on the Spot over there and fuck the shit outta him."

The woman's mouth dropped wide open. We walked off laughing, and had gotten used to people griping about how we were dressed. Maybe it was too much for kids, but the only one I was concerned about was mine. During our weekend parties, I made sure my son was away from home and at my other friend's house with her kids. He liked visiting them, and my friend didn't mind watching him while we got our business in order. I was pleased with our parties. They weren't like most events where prominent men with big names were promoting them. Instead, it was just us women. Most men liked that shit. They didn't want to attend parties being thrown by other niggas because they feared getting set up or robbed. Back then in Detroit, if I approached a group of men with a man with me, to tell them about our parties, they'd be leery of coming, especially if they had money. They assumed it was a set up where the woman would lure them into a room, pull a gun on them and take their shit. With Sweet Sensation, we didn't move like that. It was a respect thing, where the women in our clique always looked out for each other. We didn't want to risk our lives and get involved in no shady shit. That's why we were different, and as the leader, it's how I ran my operation and protected my women. That was the priority, and in my gut, I knew this was just the beginning of us making our way to the top.

Chapter Three

Getting to the top would take some time, but meanwhile, Dominic, Dallas and I lived in a two-family flat. Dallas had moved in with us because she was pretty much there all the time anyway. We had a spare room, so it was an easy transition for her to just move in. Dominic used the basement as his work area where he'd spend hours designing jackets and backdrops. The crew was set—we were all living and working together. We decided to use the upstairs of our home as the after-hours spot for parties. It wasn't because we couldn't afford another place, because we could. Being the chick on the side of Dominic, everyone in the city knew we had hella money rolling in. It was more so about being cost efficient. We knew people would feel safe and secure coming to our home for a party because of who we were. On top of that, all the money collected would go straight to us and not have to be given to a landlord for space rentals, DJs, caterers or any of that extra shit. That stuff was a waste of money, so we weren't doing that by no means. I was known in the streets for making smart decisions, also as somebody not to play with. I'd had more than a few run-ins where I had to slap a bitch for disrespecting me. But

41

between the three of us, we had solid reputations and street cred to throw these parties. Straight up live parties where the DJ mixed the beats, headphones over one ear . . . and the room dark with lights strobing for effect. We had a spacious upstairs area, so we rearranged the furniture to set it up like a club. There was plenty of room to dance and couches and chairs were strategically placed in certain spaces for lap dances. Sometimes, shit popped off way beyond being just a swinger's party or strip show. We started frying up chicken, along with other quick foods in the kitchen and selling that too. It was Dominic's idea, and in addition to attending the parties and watching me handle my business from the closet, he was also there for protection. For the longest time, we didn't need protection. But as our parties grew, one incident changed everything.

In the beginning when we were getting our parties off the ground, we held no punches whatsoever. On the few nights our parties weren't jumping, we headed to Timbow's, about a mile down the road. Timbow's was known in the D as the after-hours spot where anything goes. They had gambling, music, girls tricking in back rooms; whatever you wanted was there. So, we'd go down there and steal their girls and guys to fill up our own parties. I'd tell the girls, "Girl, you gon' make more money at my joint than you ever will up in here." Then I'd tempt the men with, "Uhn uhn, you ain't gotta go up in there. We got hotter girls right down the street."

It was word of mouth that got our parties popping, and taking from Timbow's built our business that much faster. Before I knew it, we had the hottest after-hours joint in the D. It was lit! Life for me was beginning to move so fast—you couldn't pay me to believe I wasn't living the Miami Beach lifestyle.

I didn't give a flying fuck what nobody had to say or what they thought about me. I was living a carefree life. Every single movie I watched during that time that was based out of Miami Beach had women strutting down the streets half naked in bikinis, looking as if they were walking on air without a care in the world. If me and my girls strutted on Belle Isle like they did, so what. Just because we were black women doing it in Detroit, and many of them were white women in Miami Beach, it didn't matter to me. People talked shit for sure, but their words motivated me to carry on and push harder. That's the world I was living in at the time, and I paid many of thanks to my man

Dominic. I swear if I could turn back the hands of time at least once, I'd do that shit all over again.

For over a year straight, our parties were safe and off the chain. But one particular night put a pause on everything. Up until then, we didn't need much security because we conducted pat downs at the door to make sure no one was strapped or had any weapons on them. All we had for protection was Dominic, who most of the time would mind his business in the back of the house while counting money. But that night it started with a nigga with a steering wheel in his hand. Back in the 1990s, guys who drove sweet ass, old school cars would take their steering wheel everywhere with them. It was an attempt to be flashy and prevent their cars from being stolen, so it was a cool thing to do. That's how you knew a guy was flossing in his ride, when you saw him carrying his steering wheel. So, just as things were wrapping up one night, this nigga walked in with a steering wheel in his hand, which screamed Chi-Ching. He had co-co brown skin, was slim and stood about 5'10". I noticed him while the other girls were cleaning up, and Dominic was in the back counting money. The music was still bumping in our ears, so I stepped up to the dude in my sky-high heels to see what was up.

"Can I help you with something?" I searched him with my eyes from head to toe. I'll never forget his chiseled face and a mole was on his left cheek.

"Look like the party is ova," he said, checking me out as well. "But I came here for a dance. You down or not?"

I figured it wouldn't hurt to put a few extra dollars in my pocket that night, so *why not*, I thought, before escorting him over to a chair to take a seat. As he seemed relaxed, I bent over and exposed my goods to him. My ass was clapping hard, and with his eyes bugged real wide, he appeared to enjoy my moves.

"Hell yeah!" Steering Wheel shouted and clutched his crotch. He slid money in my thong, and then squeezed a sizeable chunk of my ass. "Come get a nigga right real quick."

I turned to face him and straddled him seductively. My hands rested on his shoulders, while I grinded nice and slow on his dick. I was in my element. There was something about a good pair of high heels that made me feel sexy as hell. In the moment, I felt like I could

conquer the world then rule it.

"Is this right enough for you?" I asked while rubbing my

breasts, teasing him. I had him going crazy and could feel his dick

brick up through his jeans. No lie, I was turned the fuck on. My

nipples were erect; my juices were flowing heavy. I wanted to take

him to the backroom and wear his ass out. Normally, I didn't sleep

around unless Dominic knew about it. But because I was a freaky ass

bitch, little shit like this had a weird way of turning me on. Still,

something in my gut didn't feel right. It paid to have your eyes and

ears open in this business, and that made it easier to pick up on any

change in the wind that might come your way. Nonetheless, I ignored

the signals and proceeded to grind on Mr. Steering Wheel. As I gazed

into his eyes, I felt the hairs on the back of my neck prick. I could tell I

was turning him on by the way he dropped his head back and moaned.

He was on cloud nine as I bounced harder, but I turned around to avoid

looking into his suspicious eyes. In order to calm my suspicions, I

pictured him with that leer on his face and hoped that when I was done

working my ass off, he would pay me well.

"You like this baby? Tell me you want more," I said smiling, before turning around to face him again. That's when my smile vanished. The gun he had was aimed between my eyes, and there was a crooked smile resting on his face.

"Bitch, what I want is all yo fuckin' money, right now," he hissed through clenched teeth, while gripping my arm. "Right fuckin' now!"

I halted my movements. Pussy was drying up quick, and my mouth was wide open. He'd caught me off guard. I was too shocked and pissed off to even speak or scream. A bitch just glared at the nigga through narrowed eyes. Obviously, he didn't know who he was fucking with. No one around had even gotten a chance to scream, move or say shit because, just as ole boy yelled for me to up the money again, Dominic rushed in with a 9mm aimed and ready to shoot. His whole face was twisted, and I had never seen him look so angry.

"Muthafucka, is yo ass ready to die tonight? Get yo punk ass up and move the fuck outta here, now!"

That nigga must've saw the fire in Dominic's eyes too because he quickly pushed my ass out of the way and dashed out the door like he was trying to win a marathon. He was scared shitless, and was so afraid that Dominic was about to buss his ass, he'd left his steering wheel behind. There was no way he was coming back for it. His grimy ass thought there were only women in the house. He didn't expect to see a man inside looking out for us. Most of us were shaken by the incident, but I was too busy laughing at his scary ass running and leaving his wheel behind.

"Girl, that shit ain't funny," Dallas said, still holding her chest. She dropped back in a chair, shaking her head. "He could've killed all of us. Thank God Dominic heard that muthafucka tripping."

"What's funny is his dumb ass," I said. "How the fuck you gone be a scary ass robber? That nigga almost fell and busted his big ass head. And to know he can't even drive his car without this steering wheel is hilarious to me."

Dominic told me to toss the steering wheel to him, so I did. "I'ma sell this bitch and get some money. And if I find out who that nigga was, his ass will be dealt with. Until then, lock up and finish cleaning up. We need to talk about gettin' more security in here."

We all agreed and were relieved that things hadn't turned out bad. All I could do was laugh off the pain that day, and when I still think about it I laugh. It was the funniest shit ever, but it was also a time in our hustle when we knew certain things had to change.

The next night we partied, shit was a lot more organized and controlled because, not only did we now have lookouts, we also had paid security. They were guys we knew from our neck of the woods who worked at protecting and controlling our events. People liked the idea of having secured parties and the girls felt safer. I always looked out for them, and right around 1996, all we did was throw parties or go to parties that other people would throw. It was the beginning of a new era and definitely a good time to be in the entertainment business. I was transforming into the Madam, and life was so good to me that I started bringing people close to me in on the money. Whether it was a security guard, dancer, caterer . . . whatever, I wanted us all to get paid. Dallas was the first person to sit at the table with Dominic and me; we made sure she was well taken care of. All of us lived life on the edge for a whole year straight. But by the end of 1996, Dominic

and I decided that we were ready to conquer something else.

Chapter Four

Our new direction resulted from my reflection on the past.

Everyone who knew me always knew I'd forever be a Bed-Stuy,

Brooklyn girl at heart. My dad was from Detroit, and my mama was

originally from Brooklyn. In 1982, by the time I was five years old,

my mama lived in Detroit and my dad lived in New York. My mother

sent me to live with him for the summer and that turned into me living

with him until the age of nine.

Living with my father, who was a hustler at heart, taught me

the hustle life. He was a debonair hustler, a jack of all trades who

hustled all day. He even had a cosmetology license. While he had his

hands in all kinds of pots, his biggest hustle was with clothes. He'd

steal or swindle them, sometimes even buy them from vendors, and

then peddle them back onto the streets as a street salesman. He would

walk around the neighborhood all day until every single piece was

sold—often from eight in the morning to midnight. Sometimes, he

would take me with him. During those times, we would walk together and come up with songs. One of our very favorites was, "I ain't gon' never be hungry, I'm gonna get me some money."

By any means necessary, that's just how it was. He took me shoplifting with him in the Fashion District one day, and his eyes were sometimes bigger than his arms could carry. I couldn't believe he tried to steal a full-length fur coat. He put it underneath his jacket and started strutting towards the exit door like it wasn't shit. He didn't even notice that the fur peeked out from under his own jacket, while brushing the department store floor. I spoke up in my sweet, little girl's voice, already knowing what shoplifting entailed and realizing that he wasn't getting away with stealing that coat.

"Um, Dad, you can see it," I insisted, pointing discreetly.

He laughed and kept it moving. I don't know how he made it out of the store that day, but he did! He was the very essence of street smarts and could never give up his hustle, even when my mama told him she wasn't with it anymore. So, they split and never got back together. I lived with him and his companion at the beginning of that summer, but by the end of summer, they'd broken up. There was no one around to help him raise me anymore. His idea of raising me was being in the streets all day hustling. That shit didn't work, so he called my mama and told her he had to send me back to her. I was hampering his hustle life, basically, affecting the influx of money that came into our household. I was an only child by my mother, though I had an older sister and brother through my dad who were eight and ten years older than me. They were old enough to care for themselves; I wasn't. So, World War III popped off between my parents over how I should be raised. By the end of the conversation, my mama had turned the argument around on him. "Oh, you think you can do a better job raising her than me? Then you keep her!"

They finally settled on my dad taking me to my granddad's house instead. Granddad died a millionaire but lived as a pack rat. His house looked like something out of *Hoarders*, and he smelled like he hadn't washed his ass in years. He even had a dog who only contributed to the stench and filth. But to my surprise, Granddad owned and had made his money owning brownstones. No matter how much money he had, though, I certainly didn't want to live with him. When my dad attempted to drop me off that day, he complained about how nasty the house was.

"Man, do you ever clean this muthafucka up!" he yelled, as we stood near the doorway. Sadness covered my face, and I kept my hand clenched to my dad's because I didn't want him to leave me there.

"What you talkin' bout, fool?" Granddad said. "This place is clean. It's as clean as it's gon' get!"

He plopped down in a busted up leather recliner that was leaning to the side. The dog lay next to him on the floor, tearing into a dirty bone. Pondering what to do, my dad had to decide between leaving me there in filth or to take me back to the streets with him. He turned, kneeled down in front of me and cleared his throat.

"Listen, baby girl." He moved my long hair away from my sad eyes to look at me. "I gotta go make this money, so I'ma let you stay with yo Granddad for a little while. It won't be long, and the two of you gon' have lots of fun. You can play with the doggie and watch as much TV as you want."

A mean mug covered my face and tears welled in my eyes. He knew nothing about staying with my Grandad would be fun, and I was upset with him, and my mama, for sending me there.

Unfortunately, my dad didn't show up again until a week later. By then, my hair was nappy as fuck and my feet were black as coal. I hadn't bathed at all, and if my Granddad didn't even wash his own ass, he damn sure didn't force me to wash mine. Another argument between them ensued. My dad was pissed as he stood in the kitchen seeking answers.

"Why in the hell is she looking like that? You couldn't even take care of her for one damn week!"

Granddad threw his hand back at my dad and grunted while continuing to eat his meal. I sat at the table with him, eating a bowl of cereal.

"I did the best I could," he said. "If you don't like it, you can take yo child back wit' you and get the hell outta here."

My dad snatched me out of that chair and took me with him that day. I never went back. Only problem was, we didn't have no place to go. Therefore, we went to live in a shelter. It was crazy in that place, but me and the other kids got along. They loved to run their fingers through my long hair, playing in it. That was considered fun and games, and if we weren't doing that, we'd be outside running around or playing hide-and-go-seek in bunkbeds that were filled to capacity with other poor and broken people. I eventually got ringworms in my head from having so many dirty hands in my hair, playing outside in the dirt, and from all the other nasty shit found in shelters. My dad knew we had to get out of there. But before we did, he had to cut all my hair off. I was literally as bald as a man, and cried the whole time as I watched my hair fall to the ground.

"Daddy stoooop." I cried hard and tried to take the scissors from his hand. "Don't cut all of it off! I like my hair, Daddy, please don't cut no more."

"I like it too, but you can't walk around here with that shit in yo head. It'll grow back, so move yo hands before you get cut."

I moved my hands and sobbed harder and harder as piles of my beautiful, natural hair were scattered on the floor. Soon after that, my dad used his hustle money to find us a place. He hired a nanny to watch me and back to the streets he went. Less than five years later, he got arrested for theft and was locked up for a few months. My brother, David, whom I'd never even met before, came to get me and took me back to Detroit. By the time my dad got out of jail, I had a new place to call home and never looked back.

Shortly after we got back to Detroit, David moved to Las Vegas to go to college. We kept in touch a lot and were very close. We always made a pact to never let distance get in the middle of our relationship. We never did, and he was key to our next move.

Wanting to keep everything private about my new lifestyle, I never told my brother about the parties. I did, however, tell him about the jackets Dominic was known for designing. It was good hearing David's voice, and I was chilling in the basement with Dominic while talking to my brother that day.

"Shit, what's up, sis," David said on the other end of the phone. I visualized his wide smile; it made me smile, too.

"Nothing much. Just sitting here helping Dominic package up some jackets he sold. What you got up for the day?"

"What jackets?" he responded in a curious tone.

"What you mean? I thought I mentioned to you before that Dominic designed jackets and backdrops for celebrities. I know I told you that."

"Word?" I could hear the excitement building in his voice. "I ain't know that sis. That's dope!"

"Yeah, he's been doing this since before we met." I kept bragging about my man and his many accomplishments. "He does Jeans & Moët every year, has done jackets for Morris Day, LL Cool J and so many more celebrities. I still can't believe you ain't know that."

"Hell naw. Tell him that's dope. How is business going for him down in the D?"

"Real good, I guess. But it can always be better."

Truth be told, business was good, but it was beginning to slow up because the decade was transitioning into the new millennium. New trends and fads had hit the stores. The jackets weren't as hot as they used to be; the commercial rap game that performers like LL were transforming into a harder form of rap—one that didn't call for or allow glittery jackets and old-school performance wear. We had to figure out our next move before that well dried up completely. Only, up to that point, we had no idea what that next move would be.

"You guess," David said. "What you mean by that?"

I sighed and tried to avoid spilling more of the truth. "Shit, I don't know. His business is good, but just a little slow right now, that's all."

"That just means y'all ain't looking hard enough. Y'all probably just need a change or something. Shit, why don't y'all move west and try to get his shit in one of these sweet ass hotels down here on the strip? Vegas is a hotspot, especially right now. All the big names who's somebody in the industry live here. If not, they for sure stop through here."

The thought had me hyped and ready to pack. I looked over at Dominic who was standing there working his ass off. Maybe this was the new direction we'd been discussing, and I couldn't deny anything my brother had said about Vegas popping.

"Do you really think that will be a good idea?" I asked. "We've been talking about making some new moves, but we ain't never thought about moving to Vegas. That might be a dope idea."

"You damn right it is, and until y'all find a place, y'all can stay with me."

Boom! That was all I needed to hear. I discussed it with Dominic; he was all in. There was no denying that we needed to be wherever the money was at. The strip was a known hotspot for ballers and big spenders of all walks of life. It wasn't long before we left Detroit, heading to Vegas. It was just Dominic, me and my son. He was just a toddler. Dallas took over our lease, so it was an arrangement that worked out for everybody.

***

The move we'd made was with the intentions of us getting Dominic's work in one of the most infamous hotels on the strip, Caesars Palace. MGM was known for boxing matches and concerts; Caesars Palace was known for shopping and luxury. They even had a Tiffany's store. So, our top priority was to have Dominic's work inside of this specific casino because his jackets were one of a kind and definitely luxurious. While I truly thought that was possible, honestly, the whole move was quite new for me because I had been living in Detroit for many years. But there I was uprooting what I had going on to see Dominic's dreams come true. I didn't mind, though, because that's what you do when you love someone. Don't get me wrong, I loved the shit out of Dominic. This was just a very new experience for me. Living with my brother was a challenge for sure, and my dad lived in the same apartment, too. Ten years had passed since I'd last seen him. I wasn't that little girl who followed him around all the time. And he'd completely changed from what I remembered him being. Time had done a number on us, and it had definitely done one on him. He'd been heavy into drugs and had AIDS that he'd contracted from a contaminated drug needle. Deep down, I felt horrible for him. His body was so frail that he looked like a skeleton. He surely wasn't his old dapper self and would never get back to being the man I once knew.

The one thing that hadn't changed was him being money struck. Those old habits die hard as hell, and the first thing he saw when he was introduced to Dominic and his work was a money source ripe for juicing. We could barely get in the door, before he pounded his fist on the table, trying to set rules that included money.

"Y'all gotta pay to stay up in here!" he shouted. "Don't nobody live here for free!"

"We intend to pay our fair share," Dominic said, standing next to me. "We ain't come all this way to live off nobody, and I know my work will speak for itself."

My dad nodded, and after Dominic and I showed him some of his work, my dad sat back on the sofa and lit up like a Christmas tree. His whole tune and demeanor had changed.

"Yeah, y'all gon' make hella money selling that shit. What you think about that, David? That nigga got talent, don't he?"

David kept looking at Dominic's work in awe. "You damn right he do. And he couldn't have come to a better place to sell it."

Their praises made Dominic and me feel real good. And while David didn't really fuck with my dad too much, due to his trifling and money-grubbing ways, he still agreed with him about Dominic's talent and potential of making money.

After that day, the struggle became real. But Dominic and I never gave up. We pounded the pavement for weeks, trying to get Dominic's jackets into the right hands. During that time, my dad was fussing and cussing about us needing to bring in more money. All that juicing us got under David's skin; he swore he was done with Dad for good.

"Why don't you stay off their muthafuckin' backs and let them do what they gotta do," he said, yelling at my dad as we all headed to David's car. "It takes time to build shit up. You see them trying to put in the work, don't you?"

"With jackets like that," my dad said. "All kinda money should be in their hands right now. If it was me sellin' that shit, I bet'cha I wouldn't be walking my ass around here broke."

I had to speak up, because my dad just didn't get it. This was about making legit connections, not doing some fucked-up illegal shit like he had been engaged in. "We ain't broke, and David is right," I said. "You gotta give us time to make the right connections. It'll happen so cool the hell out, alright?"

My dad grunted, and instead of going with us that day, he took my son from my arms and headed back into the apartment with him.

"We gon' go back inside and watch some TV. We'll see you when you come back, and don't come back without no money."

DETROIT MADAM

One thing I could say about my dad was he was in love with his grandson. Vegas was the first time he'd ever met him, and he doted on that toddler like nobody's business.

Since the apartment we lived in wasn't far from the strip and the Convention Center, we headed there every day. The heat and Mexicans were as plentiful as the money around town, which was different from living in Detroit. But it was all just another day, another city and another dollar. This task was extremely hard, considering the fact that black people were only allowed to come in front doors on the strip and perform in the early 80s. Vegas still had residue of racism. The initial reason we moved was because money for Dominic's business was slow. Starting out down here, shit was the same. I had no choice but to get off my ass and get to it, as I remembered the song I shared with my dad, "I ain't gon' never be hungry, I'm going to get me some money." When things weren't moving as quickly as we intended for them to, that's exactly what I decided to do, which was get us some money.

I was now twenty years old with a very small frame. It was a sexy frame, though, and was more than good enough for dancing.

DETROIT MADAM

Getting into clubs in Vegas was a lot different from getting into clubs in Detroit. In Vegas, you had to weigh in. If you were overweight, you got the boot and that's just the way it was. If I'd eaten a sandwich and gained another five pounds, they would've booted my ass out the club. It was skinny girls only. I wore my hair long and curly; I kept a weave because the beauticians didn't know how to do hair in Vegas at all. I was one of the only black girls dancing in the majority of the clubs. Shit wasn't just a culture shock, but it most certainly was a world shock on my behalf. I was used to making money at my own parties, doing things my way and being the star of the show. And if I didn't want to dance, I didn't have to. Being in Vegas, though, had something else in store for me. I was no longer the center of attention. Those racist-ass rednecks weren't checking for me at all. They might've secretly liked black girls, but they weren't upfront about liking black girls at all. Yeah, I was the exotic girl to some of the patrons, but if there were only a bunch of rednecks in the club for the night, honey, I wasn't making one single dollar.

The Asian men loved white women. In Detroit, it was all about the black girls. There were a few joints that had white girls in the D, but for the most part, the money in that life was all for us. So, there I was that day, dancing next to a white woman, a Filipino woman, a Chinese woman and a Russian one. Without a doubt, I was the one with the most rhythm, even though the funky song spilling through the speakers in the background wasn't my cup of tea. The club was thick with men from all over. A few black men were sprinkled throughout, but they had ignored me too, as smoke filled the air and blue, red and green lights spun. Even spreading my legs wide wasn't enough to garner me any attention. The Russian girl next to me had numerous dollars tucked in her thong. More money was at her feet, as she barely put in the work. She had made so much damn money it was ridiculous. I even tried to move closer to her to dance, but one racist-ass white man with a scruffy beard wasn't having it.

"She doesn't need your help," he shouted. "Move out of the way! I can't see her."

"Jerry, be nice," one of his redneck friends said, laughing. "I'll give her some change. Here hun. Take this!"

He chuckled and flicked a quarter on stage. I wanted to tell him to kiss my ass, but I didn't want to lose my job. Instead, I strutted to the other side of the floor, and was able to collect a few dollars from an old white man who probably felt sorry for me. In their eyes, I wasn't the exotic girl up in the club. Just a black girl who needed to make some money fast. But in Vegas, the competition was steep. People could find whatever the hell flavor they wanted in those clubs. It would be served up on the stripper platter and on a stage right in front of you. I viewed it as a melting pot. And there was no telling what kind of money I'd make each night. Sometimes I was up a bit, but many times I was down. When a Thai chick showed up in the club, everybody was down. She was fine as fuck and took all the money. This was a wake-up call and real culture shock for me. My appeal seemed to have been stripped away, and I had to do something different in order to get paid. I'd never had a man turn me away, tell me not to touch him or refuse to let me come to his table. It was crazy. Do you know what they'll do to a nigga in the D, if he said some shit like that to a black girl? There would be Katt Williams up in that bitch daring you to, "Say it again, say it again!"

Just like every other challenge I'd faced, I kept on pushing, hoping things would change. I started connecting with the Caucasian dancers I worked with, and I can't lie . . . that shit was lit. Those bitches were into some of everything, which I liked in a good way. They would get white girl wasted off cheap liquor, and being under aged, I would do the same. A few of them became my real friends. We kicked it a lot, and they didn't hesitate to school me on how to get paid. Another reason why I gravitated towards them was because I quickly learned that black people in Vegas were so fake. They only wanted to hang around or follow behind people who were famous. I didn't do that fake shit; I was from the D. If I fuck with you then I fuck with you. I didn't care who you knew—it didn't matter to me one bit.

"Here," Tammy said, as we were in the locker room at the strip club that day. I had been feeling more energized during my performances, and as the white girls had been hyping me up on the stage, it helped me get more money. "Take these grapes, but don't eat a lot of them. They're going to make you feel good, honey, trust me I know."

I dropped the organic grapes in my mouth and couldn't believe the taste. Tammy didn't tell me they were soaked in Everclear, which was 150 liquor proof. Talk about being on my ass! That's exactly what I was. I mean, I was popping grapes left and right in that locker room.

"Wha—what the fuck is thiiiis," I slurred, and wobbled as I tried to leave the locker room and go on stage. The other girls laughed and had to carry me over to a chair.

"Honey, I gave you three damn grapes," Tammy said, giggling. "How many of those freaking bitches did you have?"

I'd had plenty, and before I knew it, my dumb ass had hit the floor and passed out. Unfortunately, I missed the whole shift and didn't make one dollar. That pre-shift turn up became the norm for us—me especially. With that liquid party in my veins, I felt more at ease shaking my ass and titties for strangers. Those grapes gave me courage to get there. Without taking them, I wasn't as free. If I wasn't drunk, I wasn't as social. I'd sit in the corner until I was called out by management or wait for a man to approach me, instead of going in for the kill to get money. Typically, I was a shy person, but like most people, my other side came out when I was drunk. Basically, I did what I had to do and what I saw fit for myself. It was wild, and made me feel like I was right back in Detroit, just taking on a new kind of experience with different friends and men.

After a while, some of the dancers and I started picking up after parties to work. We provided eye candy entertainment for high-rolling fools who wanted to turn up in the Sin City with a fine ass woman on their lap. One night, Dominic dropped a few of us off at a hotel on the strip. Bright lights were flashing everywhere; it was a buzz of the city nightlife. With stilettos on and skin-tight dresses that looked melted on our skin, we strutted inside of the pyramid-shaped hotel with a marble topped lobby that was crammed with tourists, workers and other partygoers. We were there to dance for some guy who'd just hit the lotto—literally—and all he wanted was to party the night away with a few half-naked women. According to the plan, we were just there to get the party started. Then, a few other girls were supposed to drop in to give him his happy ending. People gawked at us as we piled into the elevator, giggling and having fun.

"Bioootch, you had some more of those grapes, didn't you?" Tammy said, trying to look into my mouth. I slapped my hand over it and laughed.

"You damn right I did, but back the hell up," I said, jokingly. "Quit playing, okay. We got work to do."

Francine snapped her fingers, and then straightened her messy blond hair that flowed down her back like the rest of ours.

"Both of you need to quit playing around," she joked. "And if either of you would be kind enough to pop one of those little juicy grapes into my pretty mouth right now, I damn well will appreciate it."

Tammy always had the hook up, so she popped the grape into Francine's mouth, causing her to pucker her red painted lips and laugh so loud that a man next to her sighed. Francine inched over to him and softly rubbed his hair.

"Awww, poor baby," she whined, teasing him and tossing her hair to the side. "Looks like you ain't had no fun in a while. For fifty bucks, darling, I can give you all the fucking fun you need."

The man paused, but when the elevator opened, he rushed off and walked away like a scared puppy. We giggled, and tipsy as fuck, we staggered our way to the lottery winner's door and knocked. He opened the door, examined us and then a big bright smile appeared on his face.

"Come in, come in," he said, enthused. "You ladies are right on time. Let's get this party started!"

The second we entered the man's room, we could tell he had already gotten the party started and was rolling off something. He wasn't planning on stopping, and popped pill after pill, as we shook our asses in his face. There were several piles of little white pills spread out on the table. He tried to get us to take them, and was so damn high that he didn't realize that every time he put them in our hands, we danced over to the bed and tucked the pills underneath the mattress. We tricked his ass into believing that we were getting just as high as he was.

"Yo—you ladies are fucking wit' me, right?" He groaned and dropped his head back as I sat on his lap grinding on his dick and teasing him.

"Fucking with you in a good way," I said. "Gimmie some more of that shit. Whatever you want, I gotta have some too. That way, I can work you exactly how I want to. Me and my girls. Can't you see how ready they are?"

He lifted his slumped head and peeked around me. Tammy and Francine were feeling on each other, while laughing their asses off. They winked at his ass, and after he gave me another pill, I threw that shit over my shoulder when he wasn't looking.

"Gimmie some fucking pussy," he shouted and was becoming more aggressive with us. As he shook my arm, trying to manhandle my ass, I encouraged him to be patient.

"Calm down, damn. The other girls are coming for you, baby, and a man like you deserve more than just us."

He pushed me away from him and started erratically pacing the floor. Sweat spots were all over his shirt; his eyes were bugged. "I don't want to wait," he yelled with tightened fists. "I didn't pay to wait, so let's get this over with now!"

I tried to calm him down, especially since we hadn't been paid yet. "The other women are coming for you, baby. You just need to be patient. We're only here to dance."

"No, you said you were ready! You girls are here, so you do what I want you to do! Gimme that!"

He grabbed me again and flung my ass on the bed. As I bounced on top of it, he hurried to unleash his dick. Francine and Tammy quickly reached out to pull him away from me.

"No, no, no, sir, I don't think you understand," Tammy said, holding a tight grip on his arm. "We're not here for that. We're just here for the dancing, so you need to wait."

He snatched his arm away from her. The mean mug on his face tightened and he darted his finger at her.

"I will not wait! Do you hear me, I don't have to wait!"

I didn't give a fuck what he'd said, and I wasn't going to suck his dick or let him fuck me. The way he was acting, I kept thinking, *Oh, he's about to bring the D out of me and that ain't what he want!* In order to prevent that from happening, I had to get more aggressive with him.

"Look, man, sit yo ass down somewhere." I stood and walked over to where Tammy and Francine were. With my arms folded across my chest, I reminded that fool he was the one high as a damn kite, not us. "So chill the hell out and stop trying to cause a scene. You don't want the police to come up in here, so just wait until the other girls get here. Damn!"

As I took charge, he didn't know what to do. His eyes kept shifting from left to right, and he finally took a seat on the bed to chill. Shortly thereafter, he laid back and threw his arm across his forehead. We looked at each other, thinking the exact same thing. There was hella money on his dresser and it was laid all over the top of it. Francine nudged her head towards the dresser, and then stepped up to the bed.

"Sugar pie, are you okay?" she said, crawling on top of him. "I hope you okay and you don't want to miss out on all the fun, do you?"

As he kept mumbling something, me and Tammy tiptoed over to the dresser and started tucking the money everywhere we could. With skimpy dresses on, we didn't have much room, but that didn't stop us. I tucked the shit between my legs, in the crack of my ass, and in my shoes. The rest I just gathered in my hands, before hurrying to the door with Tammy following behind me.

"Wait for meeee," Francine yelled and hopped off the bed. She swiped up some money from the dresser and ran to the door. "Be patient, baby!" she yelled at the man. "Don't you worry yourself one bit 'cause the other girls are coming!"

We got the hell out of there and rushed down the hallway, towards the elevator. Money was sticking out of our clothes and shoes, and since the interior of the hotel was circularly shaped, people could see everything that happened on the same floor in a three-hundred-and-sixty-degree view. So, there we were, running through the brightly lit hallway with money coming out of everywhere. My heart was thumping in my ears as we ran in our stilettos, tripping over ourselves and cracking the fuck up. I just knew the man was going to call security on us; therefore, we only had a matter of minutes to get out of the hotel. But the truth was, the man was so high that I doubted he ever even got up. As for me, I vowed to never do another private party in Las Vegas again.

Chapter Five

During the day, my focus was hustling with Dominic to get his jackets in stores on the strip. That was hard ass work. It was all about pounding the pavement in the blazing Vegas heat, while wearing his jackets as natural advertisement. We went into boutiques on the strip, trying to talk them into stocking his jackets. I was worn out and marketed in my heels the whole time. Everything I knew about marketing and branding I learned from Dominic. I didn't know what that skillset was considered at the time, but what we were doing was really just grassroots marketing and branding. Those words always seemed so sophisticated and the skill behind them so complex. Nonetheless, I learned that I had it in me to market my wares with the best of them. From the Fashion Mall to Caesars Palace, we would see stars and celebrities walking around in their natural element with money to burn in their pockets. Wearing those jackets acted as a form of branding. It drew crowds of people on the strip to us, asking, "Where'd you get that from?" We were happy to tell them that Dominic had made them, and had also made them for stars. That would spark their interest, and some people ordered them, while others said they'd get back to us. Many never did, but on one occasion, we ran into Mike Tyson in a hotel. After doing our homework, we knew he would be in town for an upcoming fight, so we wore jackets with Tyson's face on the back. Truthfully, we never dreamed we'd actually run into him, but had hoped to get some business from some of his fans who were there to see him fight. We saw him exit from the back door of Caesars Palace, and when I tell you that man was probably only around 5'1", he was! I was a little taller than him in my heels. That funny little voice he was known for—he really did talk like that.

"Tyson," Dominic shouted and rushed up to him. His bodyguards wouldn't allow us to get close, but we were close enough for him to see our jackets. "Man, I hope you win tonight. Meanwhile, check this out." Dominic turned so Tyson could see the back of his jacket. "It's dope, ain't it? I make these, and if you like them, holla at me, au'ight?"

Tyson moved past his bodyguards and shook both of our hands. His grip was so tight that I swore my hand would fall off.

"It is dope," he said. "Nice and you do good work."

Dominic and I, both, were all smiles. I swear that shit felt like nothing but God and perfect timing because the minute Tyson gave us props, and told us how much he liked the jackets, we walked into a boutique store in Caesars Palace and got lucky. The shop sold a lot of unique, one-of-a-kind items. That day we also had our Marilyn Monroe jackets with us. The store owner fell in love with them. Everybody in Vegas loved them some Marilyn, and the uppity white lady at the shop figured they would sell.

"These are nice," she said, admiring the jackets in awe. "I can carry them on consignment. If they sell, you'll get paid. I'll price the Marilyn jacket at, uh, let's say five thousand dollars. Deal or no deal?"

Dominic and I looked at each other with glee in our eyes. We were happy as fuck, and we screamed at the same time, "Deal!"

The first jacket we sold in stores in Vegas was a Marilyn Monroe jacket. And yes, it sold for five thousand dollars. For Dominic and me, it was an eye opener because he'd only been selling the jackets for around five *hundred* dollars, up until that point. It was such an *oh my God, I've died and hit the lottery* kind of moment. And that's where we started at. From there, he also created Elvis jackets. The problem was the jackets were on consignment. So, we might sell a jacket and make five thousand one month, then not sell one the next month and make no money. In the meantime, Dominic connected with some of the most famous artists you can even think of, including finally meeting Prince at one of his concerts. Dominic was so obsessed with Prince that he had an engagement ring custom-made for me with Prince's emblem on it. It was all gold with diamonds that took up half my finger. The ring was some type of promise that we would, eventually, get married in a small, mostly impromptu ceremony. That was supposed to take place when we went to a Prince convention in Canada. But we were later in Canada on fake IDs, basically living the life of aliases while we were there. Dominic had changed his mind about getting married because, in all honesty, we hadn't even gone to

Canada using our real names. So how could we get married? But at that age, I blamed it on him not wanting to get married, which was an issue for us later on.

So, the night of the concert in Vegas, I wore my ring, and we rocked our Prince jackets. It was one of those nightclub jam sessions, so we got to stand literally right next to Prince. He really did smell like roses just like people had said. Everyone there was so hyped watching him perform, and as we were dancing, I saw a girl in the crowd step up to snap a picture of him. Remember, this was before cell phone cameras and selfies were a thing. I paused, shook my head and thought, *I wouldn't do that if I were you.* She wouldn't have been able to hear my warning over the loud music anyway, but within seconds, a security guard rushed over and lifted her from her feet. He was very aggressive as he carried her outside. She kept screaming and hollering that she'd done nothing wrong.

"All I wanted was a picture," she shouted while pounding the security guard's back. Her weak hits bounced off him, and when he reached the door, he tossed her ass outside. Some people laughed, others paid the incident no mind. Prince kept on doing his thing without any interruptions. Dominic and I loved every bit of it. We had

gotten close to Prince and the experience was something I would never

forget.

While my memories with Prince were good ones, there was

one celebrity in particular who I will never forget because she was the

bitch from hell. Salt n' Pepa came to town for Pepa's birthday party.

Dominic got an invite because he used to date her. They were still

cool, so we rolled up to the party in style. I made sure I was glowing

and gorgeous in my all black, silk pantsuit, knowing I would run into

his ex. The two of us figured this was the perfect networking

opportunity because we knew some of everybody who was somebody

would be present at her party. Many of them he'd already worked with

in the past. But I'd learned so much more about well-known celebs

that day. For one, it was the moment I first learned that Queen Latifah

was a lesbian. She was at the party with her girlfriend. Two, I learned

how fake most celebrities were and I never looked at them the same.

When we arrived, the party was at a hotel. Pepa had rented out

one of the large party rooms there and it was beautiful. It was nothing

less than what you'd expect for a VIP party with major stars present.

Nineties music bumped in our ears, people were dancing all around, drinks were being served and several waiters breezed around accommodating the rich and famous. As Dominic and I were standing by the bar area, Pepa stepped up to us.

"Hey, Pepa," Dominic said, hugging her. "Long time no see."

Her eyes searched him from head to toe. To say he was looking dope as fuck in his suit and crisp white shirt underneath would be an understatement.

"Hey, Dominic. Thank you for coming out. I wasn't sure if you'd come, and I'm glad you did. I've been good. How about you?"

"Nah, no problem and thank you for the invite. I just moved out west recently, so this was the perfect ice breaker for a nigga."

With a drink in her hand, Pepa cocked her head back, surprised. "Really? I had no idea you'd moved to Vegas."

"Hell yeah. Me and my girl did." Dominic slipped his arm around my waist and pulled me closer to him. "This is my girl, Kandi. Kandi this is Pepa."

Pepa, looking just as fly as she did on her album covers and magazine spreads, took a second to step back and look me up and down. This bitch had the audacity to dismiss me. She cut her eyes at me, and continued to converse with Dominic as if I didn't exist.

"So, yeah, what have you been up to?" she asked. "What you out in Vegas doing? Your jackets?"

"Yeah, and a few other things too. I . . ."

As they continued to talk, I stood there seething with anger. I was still only twenty years old at the time, and this woman, about a decade or so older than me, was treating me like I wasn't even standing there. She made me feel like I was beneath everyone there, and I had never in my life been in a situation that crazy and shallow. As bad as I wanted to show my ass Detroit style, I chose not to. I couldn't resist acting like a brat though, and all that was on my mind was, *I just got dismissed! Fuck this bitch and her birthday party. I'm ready to go!*

We stayed for another thirty minutes to an hour, and then we left. But best believe I made it my thing to never, ever, ever be put in a situation like that again. What that day changed for me was I was no longer celebrity struck. I'm not awed by them anymore, and they are just like regular people to me. Seeing how some of them treated people made me sick. Before that moment, my young ass would have run up to Pepa and said, "Oh, my God! I've heard all yo songs!" But when she did that, I was like, *oh, wow, okay.* I was determined to make myself a star rather than running behind those other stars. If someone said to me something like, "You ain't the star in every situation, Kandi." I would respond, "Shit, prove it."

After going through hell and hot water to get Dominic's jackets in a store, achieving that actually forced me to pick up my hustle times ten. Unfortunately, we had to wait to get more sells on his jackets, in order for us to make more money. By this time, I was dancing fulltime, while he was out trying to hustle his jackets. I had no time to enjoy the benefits of having his jackets in that store, and I felt exhausted from putting in so many hours at the club. I had been in contact with my mama, since I'd moved to Vegas. She sensed something was wrong, and when I called to give her an update one day, at first, all she'd done was listen. I didn't want to tell her everything because I knew she'd be worried. But after talking to her for so long, I ended up telling her that I'd picked up dancing shifts to make some extra money.

"Hey, mommie," I said in a somber mood. "What are you doing?"

"Hey baby. I just got done washing clothes and watching the news. All I can say is it's some crazy ass people out there, so be careful. How's everything going in Vegas?"

"It's going okay. Little issues here and there, but nothing too big to worry about."

"That's not what the sound of your voice says. I can tell something is wrong. What's wrong, Kandi? Is it the jackets?"

She was throwing one question after another at me. I just didn't know what to say. "Well," I said then paused.

"Talk to me, baby. It's okay. Tell me what's going on."

I released a deep breath and explained the situation to her. "The jackets are selling, but they just going slow right now. We finally got them into a store, but until business picks up, I'm dancing full time."

"Well, baby, sometimes you gotta do what you have to do to make ends meet. Just stay strong. It will all pay off in the end. I know it will."

Tears welled in my eyes. A part of me felt relieved for being honest with her about what I had been doing, and I appreciated her support. The thing about my mama was she'd always hear people out and listen to what they had to say. But after she slept on that shit, she'd wake up ready for war. The next day, she called everybody, fussing and cussing about what I had been doing. Dominic, David and I had already gotten a new place, and she called him first. With David standing next to him, Dominic stood in the kitchen with the phone held away from his ear. I could hear what my mom was saying to him.

"Dominic, if you can't take care of my daughter and my grandson the way I've been taking care of them, then you need to send their asses home! And where in the hell is David? I thought he said there was gonna be work down there and you'd be able to get those damn jackets in more stores! Ask David why in the hell is his sister on a goddamn stripper stage then?"

She must've slammed the phone down, because it went dead. Minutes later, my dad called and said she had cussed his ass out, too. Because I was a brat, I was the only one she hadn't said anything to. I stood back with my arms folded, shaking my head at it all. My dad, however, defended me. Whatever I wanted to do, he stood behind me. If I wanted a free-for-all, a free-for-all I would have. So, she cursed his ass out just because he wasn't being a good father in her eyes. I truly didn't believe that to be the case, but I couldn't be mad at my mama for being concerned.

Right after that incident, I picked up a part-time job through a temp service, so I switched to dancing only on the weekends. The fact that my mama was on my back took a toll on me. I didn't want her flying to Vegas. I knew that if she came across country to get me, some shit would hit the fan. Then again, she didn't have to come for shit to hit the fan. The boutique shop in Caesars Palace where Dominic's jackets were ended up closing down.

Chapter Six

One thing I'd have to say about our time living in Vegas was it wasn't all about jackets, strip clubs and celebrity parties. Our swinger's lifestyle really switched into a new gear, and swinging in Vegas was, and still is, practically a damn artform. At that point, I'd been around sex and nudity too long to even be phased by it. Even then, some parties were still gross as hell to me. Like one particular party I'd gone to that was thrown by an old white man and his younger woman. The woman was off the chain; she took swinging to a whole new level. There was a line of men waiting for her to give them oral sex. Literally, a long line of men from different races. She was taking them one at a time, and sucking their dicks until they came on her oversized, fake-ass breasts. Then, the next man would walk up and shove his dick in her mouth. While on her knees, she'd moan as she went to work on it. Once the man nutted, she'd be so thrilled that she tossed her long hair back, closed her eyes and lathered her breasts with sperm. The line went on and on with all of them squirting on her breasts, until they were covered in thick, white cum. Other people stood around as voyeurs.

"Cheers," she said, as a black man scooped cum off her breasts and put it into a cup. Nearly everyone laughed, with the exception of me. I just stared in disbelief.

She stood and clapped her hands, as a signal to let everyone know the *show* was over. "It's time for you all to go so my darling hubby and I can finish up. Like always, it's been a pleasure."

We were all kicked out of the room, and all I could think that night was, *which one of them drank the nut?* I assumed the nigga had done it, because if she was going to do it, she would have done it right there. We'd already watched her choke down ten dicks back-to-back. Why not a cup of cum, too? That shit grossed me the hell out. It was too much for me, and I told Dominic he would never see me do no crazy shit like that.

Another time, we attended a swinger's party with one of the white girls I danced with and her black boyfriend. Like some swinging couples, they had rules with their shit. The rule was no tongue kissing or lying up with the person they were swinging with—nothing intimate. It had to be all about and only about the sex. While we were in the midst of partying, she messed around and kissed the man she was fucking. Her man saw that shit and snatched her hair, gripping it tight.

"What the fuck are you doing?" he shouted and hurried to pull his dick out of the woman he was fucking. "Do you not want to abide by our rules?"

She looked at him with confusion all over her face. Before she could say anything, the dude she had been fucking spoke up.

"It was my fault," he said. "I was the one who kissed her first."

The black dude wasn't having it. Next thing I knew, he slapped the shit out of both of them. In shock, my eyes grew wide. I was like, *Damn, that's harsh!* To me, they were allowing the most precious parts of themselves to be penetrated and touched. Kissing wasn't shit compared to that. But for them, that was a rule they were supposed to follow. She'd broken that rule, and as a heated argument ensued, Dominic and I gathered our shit and left. We didn't have time for chaos. For us, swinging was strictly about one thing and one thing only, and it damn sure didn't involve fighting.

DETROIT MADAM

Even as we were getting deeper into the swinging lifestyle, I was still learning that there was a whole sex culture in Vegas that I needed to stay away from. Pimp culture was, and still is, real there. As the months went on, I noticed more and more of my friends were telling me to never look a man—who you didn't know—in the eye in Vegas. If it turned out he was a pimp and you, as a woman, looked him in the eyes, that would signal that you chose him. You were giving the okay for him to choose you back, and if you weren't looking for a pimp, then that wasn't what you wanted. It was a weird adjustment for me because I'm someone who's all about eye contact. I'll look someone in the eyes to decide whether they're telling me the truth or not. That's just how I was raised. I was raised on the mentality that if a person couldn't look you in the eyes, they're shady. By "choosing" a pimp, that meant you were free for their taking, which could mean kidnapping, sex trafficking or worse. Just from a look in the eyes.

Keeping that in the back of my mind at all times, once Dominic and I had put down roots and got used to our way of life in Vegas, Dallas came out to visit us for her birthday. We all went to the mall to go shopping. Dominic was off somewhere in another department,

91

while Dallas and I were looking at shoes. We were shocked when a fine-ass man dripping in jewelry, with a fur coat on, came up to her gushing about how beautiful she was. He was fit and tall. We both were so mesmerized by him, and there were several girls around him.

"Hey beautiful," he said softly while staring into her eyes. "What'chu out here doin'?"

Dallas glanced at him and the girls with a shy smile. "I'm just out here for my birthday, shopping with my girl. What's up?"

He touched her chin, and started running game hard.

"What's up is, what are you doing tonight? How long are you planning to be here, and why don't you let me send you out with my girls."

I'd heard enough and whipped my neck around so fast that I damn near broke it.

"Sorry, but she ain't interested in going nowhere with you and yo girls. Have a nice day, sir, and goodbye."

He ignored me and kept looking at Dallas, waiting for her to respond. She was slipping into a trance, so I grabbed her arm, pulling her in another direction.

"Girl, wa—wait a minute," she said. "What are you doing? That man was just being nice. I might wanna go party with him tonight. His ass was fine!"

"Trust me when I say that you don't want none of that. His ass is a pimp. They be out here kidnapping girls, and if you go meet up with him, I probably won't see yo ass again! I mean, they be on some 'you won't see yo people for months' type kidnapping."

Dallas laughed her ass off and didn't believe one word I'd said. You know us D girls were always trying to be the hardest. It was hard to convince us of anything.

"Girl, that nigga ain't gone kidnap me!" Dallas insisted. "Stop playing and let me go back over there to see what's up."

As she pivoted, I grabbed her again and dragged her ass as far away from that store as I could. We never looked back, and even years later, we still sat around and joked about her being the "chosen" one. It was a good thing that she didn't challenge me that day. I can only think about if she had, what would have ultimately happened to her. Vegas was one hell of an experience, but at that point, I was ready to make a move back to Detroit.

Chapter Seven

No doubt, I was grateful to have had the opportunity to move around and see other places, but I couldn't have been happier to see Detroit in my life than when we got back from Las Vegas. The year and a half we'd spent there was more than enough for me. I was ready to go back home—to our real home.

Don't get me wrong, Vegas was a very beautiful place, but I just could not take the year-round heat, and the people living there wore me out. There weren't many black people in sight, and I was tired of the overall fakeness of the city. So, back to Detroit we went. Because Dallas had taken over our lease, Dominic and I had moved back in with her. Her boyfriend had moved in with her, too, so the place was a bit crammed. We made it work, though, and shortly after moving back home, I was pregnant again.

Dominic already had a daughter from his previous marriage, and with him and my son being so close, he didn't want any more kids. He'd already been having issues with his daughter's mom, and even though his daughter had visited us when we got our own place again, I never really understood what their custody situation was. Dominic and his ex were many years older than me, both were in their thirties at that point. I was never really involved in what they had going on with their daughter; I just let him handle it the way he saw fit. However, there were times when I'd nudge him and tell him he needed to go pick his daughter up and be more involved in her life. He usually wouldn't budge because he didn't want to have to deal with his daughter's mom. Now, we had to deal with the pregnancy; we went back and forth about it for months. There was so much tension in our household, because he wanted me to have an abortion.

"You already have a son," he said while sitting on the edge of the bed. "I don't want no more kids and you gotta think about how I feel about this shit too."

"Hell, that's all I ever think about," I yelled and stomped towards the door with my jacket in my hand. We had been arguing all day about the shit, and there seemed to be no way for me to get through to him. "I want this baby. An abortion is not an option for me. Don't you know how much doing something like that will affect me?"

"I do know, but we just got back home. We ain't even settled yet, and we barely got enough money to stay on our feet. This shit will be much harder with an extra mouth to feed. Why the fuck can't you see that?"

"Then all that means is we just have to work a little harder than we already do. This is our baby. My baby and I'm excited about it. I've always wanted a girl, and I hope this is one."

Dominic stood his ground, and after going back and forth on this matter for so long, at five months pregnant we decided it was best if I had an abortion. I was heartbroken, and didn't even realize things could get so much worse. It did, particularly when I had to deal with the two-day abortion procedure that left me bitter and numb. It was one of the worst experiences of my life. I mean that shit from the bottom of my heart. I was traumatized behind it, and I vowed to never put myself through anything like it ever again. To this very day, I have upheld my self-commitment.

The first day I went in for the abortion, they prepped me and gave me medication to take to start the process. I'd never had an abortion before, which was both physically and emotionally painful enough. The fact that the process was so long made it even worse. Emotionally, it was traumatizing for me because I've always been a Christian. So, I had so much guilt and self-doubt running around in my head. There were voices screaming how wrong I was, how I shouldn't have even been in that room contemplating doing such a thing to my own baby. Physically, there was the very real pain of losing a baby, of my body reacting and readjusting to what was basically a delivery. Cramps. Bleeding. It was all so bad. And I couldn't even take the time to recuperate from it all, because I had to stay moving. I had to stay working, even if it was just to take my mind off everything. So, after the abortion, I went right back to work, waitressing, for a time, until I started doing nails a skill I learned right after high school. Dominic went back to making jackets and backdrops and we had made enough for us to move into a new place, and our next move was on Sussex, off Grand River and Fenkell. I wasn't sure if this move was for the better or worse, but I couldn't deny the bitterness I harbored inside of me. It just wouldn't dissipate as quickly as I wanted it to, and it drove a wedge between me and Dominic. More so, it caused me to venture out and do other things that didn't always include him.

DETROIT MADAM

One of my girlfriends from high school, Sheila, owned a nail salon inside of Mammoth, which was similar to a strip mall. It was all in one seven-floor building and had every service in the world from hair salons, nail salons, clothing, jewelry, tattoo artists, literally, every service you could think of was inside of this place. Initially when we moved back to Detroit, I was no longer dancing or hustling on my own, so Dominic was basically footing the bills. Even though we still had money left over from Vegas, and Dominic was still designing jackets and backdrops, I decided to start doing nails in Sheila's shop for two reasons: one, to get out of the house and finally have a *life* of my own, and two, to have my own money in my pocket.

Yes, Dominic was the love of my life and, outside of my son, I adored him more than anything in life. But damn, a bitch needed her own space and I needed that shit bad. We were around each other 24/7. He took me and my girls everywhere, did everything with us . . . and was always in my space. My 'me' time was more than needed. The perfect getaway was me working in the nail salon. Not only did I need the 'me' time, but soon after I started doing nails, I realized how under his control I had been. I wanted so much more out of my life. At this time in my life, I didn't even drive. I didn't do anything by myself. If I wanted to go to the store, Dominic drove me. If my girls and I went out at night, Dominic was with us. Being twenty-one, I was starting to realize that I didn't have my own identity. My entire identity was me and Dominic. It had been that way ever since I was eighteen years old. Remember, he'd even picked out my clothes. I didn't really have a say of my own. If we went to the mall, I never said, *Oh, I want that 'fit.* Instead, it was always me saying, "Dominic, I want that 'fit. What do you think?"

But as a twenty-one-old, I certainly didn't feel like it. I'd been through too much in my life already, and I'd never really been able to do kid shit. We had fun—don't get me wrong—but I had never lived with the luxury of that kind of freedom. I'd always watched my girls go out together for girls' nights and it was never a second thought in my mind. But when I went out, it was always me and Dominic.

At the same time, we were going into another year, and people just weren't into designed jackets and backdrops no more. Trends had shifted with the times as they always eventually did. So that particular stream of income was slowly but surely decreasing again and for good this time. Dominic had to come up with something new to do, and that's when he'd found a new hustle that was illegal and dealt with fraud. He started making fake IDs, which brought him a great deal of income. With the start of the 21st century approaching quickly, Detroit decided to change the look of their IDs and add holographic wording. This new technique made it harder for people to make fake IDs, or so they thought it did. The task would have been hard for anybody, but Dominic, who was an art genius, found a way to duplicate the process perfectly. So, it had gone from him hustling jackets to him hustling fake IDs. Business was booming yet again, but in a different way. His new partner in crime was his best friend's brother-in-law, Santino.

Now this nigga was the definition of fine, for real. Because of his obvious Dominican features, caramel brown skin and long pretty hair that he always wore in a ponytail, Dominic considered him a pretty boy. That meant, he didn't too much allow me to be around him. Regardless, his insecurities didn't stop Santino and me from digging each other. We were digging each other hard, too, but because of the love and loyalty I'd had to Dominic, I locked myself in for a little more time with a man who, at the time, I didn't realize had major jealousy, insecurity and manipulation issues. Those issues caused us to argue time and time again about Santino.

"All I'm saying is I don't like the way you keep looking at that nigga," Dominic said. "I can tell you want to fuck him. The look in yo eyes say exactly what yo ass be thinking."

I was in the kitchen cooking and really didn't have time to entertain an argument with him about this. I also couldn't believe that my attraction to Santino was that obvious. I tried to play it down like it wasn't.

"How many times do we gotta talk about this? When Santino come around, I barely say anything to him. You act like him and me been fucking or something. Be careful what you accuse somebody of, 'cause you know you can force them to do something they ain't even thinking about doing."

My words were upsetting to Dominic. He walked over to the stove where I was and became more aggressive.

"You betta not ever fuck around with that nigga and I find out about it. If you do, you gon' start some shit up in here that ain't gon' be good for neither of us."

I wasn't sure if that was a threat or not, but I was sure to watch myself around Santino. He was around all the time, and would bring Dominic new people who needed his services. And every time he would look my way or say something nice to me, I would try my best to ignore him.

"Girl, you got it smelling really good up in here," he said, complimenting me while him and Dominic sat in the living room. "I hope I can get a taste of that."

I wanted him to get a taste, but not of the food I was cooking. All I did was smile, especially when I saw Dominic looking at me and waiting for me to say something. I kept my word about being loyal to him, and that only changed when our relationship came to a screeching halt.

See, Dominic and Santino were the highest paid fraudulent tag team in the city of Detroit. If people were cashing checks, they'd come to them for fake IDs. If people were involved in credit card fraud, they'd be right at our doorstep. The environment of people we were around started to change, which was an eye-opener for me. I didn't like it one bit, and since the abortion had already carved a rift between us, I seriously wanted out. It was time for a change, and I started thinking more about going to school and one day getting a law degree. At the end of the day, I had been doing that dancing and hustling shit for fun. I wasn't doing it as a long-term lifestyle, and I needed to set goals for myself because doing so would help me make a difference in life.

I needed to do that for myself, because there was always something inside of me that believed black kids didn't get to do anything for fun. For white kids, society has everything carved out for them. When they fuck up or act out it's, "Oh, they were just living a little fun. They've been really on edge recently." But when it came to black kids, we're just "bad." Bad apples that need to be punished. So, I looked at my life as us just having fun, as us being able to live a certain lifestyle and express our freedom. We were wearing whatever. We were doing wherever. But by then, the sparkle was starting to fade from that lifestyle. The people I'd gone to high school with were all in college. They were living the college life; they didn't have kids. All I was doing was partying, without really earning anything for it. I felt I could have earned more, if I'd chosen a different path. What I was doing wasn't steady or consistent. It wasn't enough for me to build a life on this and to hook my hopes on it. I really started questioning my purpose. School would give me a fresh new start, and I decided to approach Dominic about it. That day, I was looking jacked with rings on my fingers and looking way older than my twenty-one years. I thought back to that night in Canada when Dominic didn't want to get married. That still bothered me, too, and I knew I needed to do *something* to change the way my life was going.

"School," Dominic shouted as we drove to the store. "Shit, we already making good ass money. What the fuck you need that for?"

"What do I need what for?" I asked sarcastically. "A fucking education?"

He shook his head and cut his eyes at me. "Look man, I don't give a fuck what you say. I ain't paying for that shit so you can get that idea out yo head. Better yet, stop asking me to pay for the shit. Damn!"

He slammed his hand on the steering wheel, causing me to jump. I don't know why my asking him to pay for school made him so upset, but it did.

"All that ain't even necessary," I said. "You act like I'm asking you to risk yo life for me, when all I'm asking for is money to pay for school. Something is really wrong if you don't even want to do that. Please tell me what it is, 'cause I'm fucking confused."

Of course, he couldn't answer my question. Something was very wrong with this, because if I asked him for five thousand dollars for some jewelry or any other frivolous shit, he'd hand it over without a second thought. But asking for five thousand dollars to go to school—to better myself, to educate myself—that wasn't cool with him. I couldn't take it anymore. It was driving me crazy, and the longer I sat around and allowed him to control my destination, I was just prolonging my progress. I knew I had to jet. In the back of my mind, I felt like Dominic was worried about me outgrowing him. Because he didn't go to college or further schooling, he didn't want a young girl who was yearning for higher learning. That was the real reason behind him saying no, and why he acted a fool every time I touched on the subject. No matter how much it annoyed him, I kept on asking him to pay for it. Then, one conversation in particular revealed everything and let me know what really mattered to him. His insecurities, controlling ways and manipulation were beaming loud and bright through his skin. It tore me into pieces, and the conversation we'd had involved swinging. I was genuinely ready to end our lifestyle as swingers, and he would not budge. I mean, don't get me wrong, I enjoyed our lifestyle a lot and, yes, we'd been doing it since the beginning of our relationship. But because I was getting older, I was feeling like it was very superficial. It just wasn't for me anymore. We were starting to hear about people we knew catching HIV, and it started to dawn on me the fact that our relationship had never been about just me and him. There had always been someone else involved. Other dicks involved; other pussies involved. During the entire relationship, we either lived with my brother or Dallas. It was rarely ever just us, and it wasn't the future I envisioned for the woman I wanted to become. That consisted of being a college educated entrepreneur. With that in mind, I knew an end to that lifestyle was near. As a matter of fact, I wasn't even living my own lifestyle; I was living *his lifestyle*, where there was no structure or no boundaries at all. We didn't have steady jobs to get up and go to. We were waking up whenever the hell we felt like it, drunk. Two drunks with money that no longer satisfied me. I was no longer satisfied with him giving me money here and there. I wanted my own life, my own money, my own career, and it started to be about . . . me.

The epiphanies I had started coming faster and faster, harder and harder. I would have probably ignored the signs, but this situation shed more light on what I already knew. We likely would've eventually grown apart anyway, based on the foundation of the relationship we'd built and how shaky it already was. And maybe I would have stuck through it longer, if he'd paid for me to get an education, but that wasn't the case. More arguments occurred, but I'd made excuses for him because he'd never grown up with structure, only chaos.

For one, I'd be lying if I said I didn't understand where Dominic's control issues and insecurities had come from. He needed to control situations that weren't really his to control. He knew he had brothers and sisters out there from his dad's side, but he only met one of them one time. He never knew his father. His mother was a drug addict. Dominic and his sister would sit in the living room as children while their mama went in the bathroom to shoot up. They could predict if she was getting high or not by how long she stayed in the bathroom. He was eight or nine years old when he lost his mother in his arms to a drug overdose. She'd shot herself up with a needle in the neck. Dominic walked in the bathroom one day, after she had been in the bathroom for far too long. He'd thought he may have even heard her fall and hit the floor because there was a loud thump that got his attention. That's when he went into the bathroom and found a needle hanging out of her neck, while she silently passed away on the floor. Ever since then, he'd had issues with people leaving him. I surely didn't want to, but pertaining to our situation, he'd brought it all on himself.

If that wasn't enough, I found out Dominic had cheated on me. It wasn't the typical kind of cheating where the guy lies until going to his grave to cover it up. Dominic cheated and then he told me about it. But for me, that was all I needed to have a final excuse to leave. In our situation, cheating was a double violation because that was a violation of something *he* put together, rules *he'd* set to make our swinger lifestyle justifiable and okay with the both of us. So, as we were in the middle of one of our heated arguments that day, I gave him an ultimatum.

"Since you cheated," I said as we stood outside. He was standing by his car and was on his way to go *handle* some business. "You either stop swinging altogether, or you lose our relationship."

He was so nonchalant as he opened the car door and shrugged his shoulders. Seriousness was trapped in his eyes; he real was blunt. "I cheated 'cause all you been doing lately is running off at the mouth and harassing me about paying for school. That's dumb shit and I ain't never gon' waste my money on no shit like that. If you wanna go, you pay for it. And if you giving me an ultimatum about swinging, you already know what I'ma choose."

"You damn right I know, so don't expect me to be here when you get back. You can have all of this shit. Nigga, I'll get my money for school, and so much more than that!"

Dominic damn sure didn't have the faith in me, but I guess he didn't know me as much as I'd thought he did. The smirk on his face said it all, as he hopped in the car and sped off. I marched my ass right inside of our house and started packing my shit. Tears welled in my eyes, but my gut told me the timing was right and this was exactly what I needed to do.

Deep down, I knew Dominic couldn't stop swinging. It had become a need for him way before we'd even gotten together. So his choosing swinging over me wasn't a surprise. I was, however, surprised when he came back that day so we could try to settle our differences. It was too late, though. My mind had already been made up about leaving him. The argument had ceased and we had calmed down while lying in bed, listening to Ex-Factor by Lauryn Hill on repeat. Dominic tried to shame me for betraying him.

"You don't love me anymore, do you?" he cried while holding me in his arms. He held onto me for dear life. "And if you can just up and leave me like this, you don't know what love is."

I turned to face him and reached over to wipe his wet face. Tears were welled in my eyes too. Leaving him was painful for me, and seeing him so emotional almost caused me to change my mind.

"That's not true, Dominic. This just ain't for me no more, and I'm tired of arguing with you about what I need to do with my own life. I love you with my whole heart, but it's time for you to let go of me so I can finally fly like I want to."

He ignored me and loosened his hug from around me. His intention was to make this all about me betraying him, so he kept on bashing me, hoping I'd feel guilty.

"You betrayed the fuck outta me. I'll never love another bitch because of you. You leaving me just like everyone else did. Don't you never say you love me again, 'cause you don't know what the fuck love is."

I wasn't going to spend my last night with him, trying to convince him that I did. He knew I damn well did, and after all the shit I'd done for him, it was an insult that he could even say that shit to me. By the very next morning, I had packed me and my son shit and was ready to move the fuck on. The second I opened the front door, I sucked in a deep breath, let the cool breeze slap my face and stepped into a new life that was waiting for me.

Chapter Eight

I always like to say that God watches over and protects me. That turned out to be true in the case of me leaving Dominic, because about six months later, the FBI started watching him. Later, a rain of indictments would fall down, and about a year after I left him, they arrested him. By that time, I was closing in on twenty-two years old, and was now a single mother learning to live life on my own. The day after I'd left Dominic, I moved back in with Dallas and her boyfriend. Even though their relationship was shaky, and they argued all the time, I hung in there until I could afford to live on my own. Once again, it was a real struggle for me. I had even asked Dominic for money, but he wouldn't give it to me, unless I went back to him. That didn't happen, and day by day, I'd made progress. One of the first things I'd done was save money to purchase a car for me and my son to get around in. I went to the bank to deposit one hundred and twenty dollars that day, and had accidentally entered an extra zero into the machine. The bank credited my account with the full twelve hundred dollars, and back then, the computer system at the bank wasn't set up to match the funds I'd actually deposited. I wasn't sure what to do, but needing a car so badly, I withdrew the twelve-hundred-dollar credit and decided to use it as a down payment. Just as I was about to leave the house and go look at cars, a representative from the bank called me.

"Ma'am, we're so sorry, but we made a mistake with your bank credit. You deposited one hundred and twenty dollars but was credited twelve hundred dollars. I see that you've already withdrawn the funds. Can you go back into the bank and deposit the additional funds you received?"

At that point, I was too hyped about getting my car and wasn't going to return shit. "Oh, I'm so sorry. I did withdraw the money, but I already spent it on bills. Can I make some type of payment arrangements to pay it back?"

I could hear the disappointment in her voice. "I guess you'll have to. This is what you need to do . . ."

I wasn't going into the bank to make any type of arrangements, but I did set up a payment plan with the woman over the phone. Afterwards, I drove to a car lot and got a car. It was a good feeling, because it was one of the first times I had done something on my own. Yeah, the bank situation helped, but I looked at it as a loan.

Having a car helped me stay away from the chaos that was happening almost every single day with Dallas and her boyfriend. My son and I were trying to get some sleep one night, and all we could hear was glass breaking and hollering. I held my son close to me and promised him that we would get our own place.

"Please mommie," he said tearfully. "I don't want nobody to get hurt. We won't get hurt, will we?"

"No baby. I won't let that happen and you can count on that. I'm gon' get us a house so you can have yo own room, okay?"

He looked up at me with his beautiful eyes, smiled and nodded. "Okay. Can you decorate my room with Batman? You know I like Batman, don't you?"

"Yeah, but I thought you liked Spiderman too. Either way, Batman it is."

I hugged him tighter and was determined to keep my promise to him. Less than a month later, I did move out, but we still didn't have a place of our own. My dad and stepmother had moved back to Detroit months ago, so we went to go stay with them. It was better than living with Dallas and her man. Their constant fighting, her moving in and out, whether it was to get his attention or because she really felt like each time she left she'd stay gone, was crazy. I thanked them for letting me stay and wished them well on my way out the door.

My dad and stepmother lived in the hood, so it was a different environment for me. But at the same time, I felt free. It was the first time I was driving where I wanted, on my own, and buying the clothes *I* wanted to wear without having to ask someone their opinion or permission.

The only rule my dad and stepmom had for me was if I was going to go out at night, I had to make sure my son was asleep first. The type of money I was accustomed to, in Detroit, you could only get that one of three ways: working at a plant, selling drugs or dancing. I wasn't going to work in no plant and I couldn't deal drugs, so I opted to go back to dancing instead.

I started school during the day at WCCC while dancing at night to provide for myself and my son. The Sass Key was the first club I danced at in Detroit, which was a very humbling experience for me.

DETROIT MADAM

Back in Vegas, that city was filled with nothing but ballers and high rollers. Once I'd learned the ropes, the tips came easy. I had gotten used to getting paid big-time money to take my clothes off and strip on the nights that were good. Whereas now in the D, shit wasn't so much the same. These raunchy ass, poor . . . living in their mama's basement ass niggas wanted you to strip, dance, split, flip, climb the pole, and do tricks, only for you to look down and see they'd tipped you one dollar! All of that for one fucking dollar. It amazed the fuck out of me; I can't even lie! There was no making it rain at all—that was bullshit. To get money up in those clubs, I really had to do some work.

Nonetheless, The Sass Key was well known throughout the city for having top celebrities drop in on certain occasions and spend big dollars. So, I was able to connect with artists in the city and expand into doing paid parties. At first, I didn't start creating my own parties; I started by going to parties. And there was this thing in Detroit where when you danced in the clubs, you had to tip out. That meant you had to pay for your time dancing based on whatever time you arrived. Clubs opened around eight, so every girl was expected to work from eight to two. So, if we got there at eight, or if it was a slow night, our tip out might be thirty to forty bucks. If we didn't show up until eleven or twelve at night, number one, we might not be able to dance because there'd already be fifty-eleven girls there. But if we were able to dance, then our tip out might be a little higher. On a good or banging night, we could easily have to pay one hundred dollars or more before leaving. Even if we wanted to leave early, before the club closed, we'd have to pay extra tip out to be allowed to leave.

Then, when it came to the private parties, there were still men in Detroit who had been throwing parties since back in my swinger party days. They knew fifty-eleven dancers to bring to all of their parties. That meant that we had to get there at exactly the right moment, if we wanted to dance in those private parties for money. If we got there too late, homegirl next to us would've already cleaned them niggas out. There wouldn't be any money left to make. Something about this way of business had to change, and it was when I realized that if I was hitting up multiple parties a night to dance at, there really wasn't a way for me to make enough money. I was always getting to the parties later than the other girls were. The money wasn't guaranteed. It was the luck of the draw. I didn't like luck of the draw.

I knew what my bills were every month; therefore, I couldn't be out there trying to get lucky at parties. So, I started doing my own thing. It started from men I'd met at clubs requesting me at their parties, and me flipping it on them to say, "Well, how about you pay me to put the whole party together for you. No stress on you and all you have to do is get your boys together and just show up and party."

A huge fan of mine named Richard liked that idea. He kept interrupting me that day, while I was trying to work and get money. "That sounds like a masterplan," he said. "Tell me more about how you can set that shit up, and how many girls will come with you?"

"As many as you want. Just tell me and I'll make sure they come. The shit will be lit and you'll wanna throw these parties all the time. I can handle it, trust me."

Richard was down for the idea, but I was skeptical about setting up parties for some other people. One in particular was a big time rap group who would always come through the Sass Key and show me mad love. They wanted to book me to do their private parties, and although they were cool, them niggas did heavy coke. I didn't want to be nowhere around that shit, so not once did I ever take them up on their offer or suggest planning a party for them. I had the idea of doing this on my own and doing it the right way. Once word got around that I was dancing in the Sass Key, shit was on and popping. People started to come see me, specifically, and I would share my next move with them.

For my twenty-second birthday, I had a big ass party that everybody who was somebody in the city at the time rolled through. It was standing room only. Now, this wasn't no Kash Doll "26 in one night" kinda party, but best believe for my twenty-second birthday in '99, them bitches "couldn't top me." All my girls knew I'd been in Vegas for a while, where none of the girls had to have any skills whatsoever to strip. All we had to do was look pretty, so my girls were always teasing me at the club.

"I bet you can't do the pole!" Kay said. "I bet you can't do it, and I will pay big dollars to see you climb that bitch!"

"You must don't know who you talking to," I said, laughing from the alcohol I had been tossing back. I'd had so much liquor in me that I was game for anything. "And if you watch my moves tonight, you just might learn something. Now, move the hell outta my way."

I playfully shoved her aside, and marched on stage like I owned it. Before I even hit the floor, money started dropping everywhere. Niggas knew it was my birthday, so they came out to show me extra love. I gave them something in return and worked the shit out of that pole. It was so crazy that night, my cousin and sister had to come into the dressing room with garbage bags to help me secure all the money I'd made. It felt so good to put all the money I'd made into my own pockets, but to be wholeheartedly truthful about everything, Dominic and I were done, but he still held a huge influence over my life. This was before he'd been arrested. He would still watch my son while I worked at night. I would go drop him off, and Dominic would do dumb ass honoree shit like come to the door in a full-length mink in the hot ass summer. Everyone knew I'd always wanted a full-length mink coat, so he'd wear it to taunt me.

"Look at all this fine nigga right here that you done gave up," he said, turning in a circle so I could check him out. He did look sexy as hell, but just not sexy enough for me to change the path I was on.

"Nice coat," I said as I watched my son go inside. "Be sure to let me know where you got it from, 'cause I plan to get me one in the near future too."

The nigga still didn't have no faith in me. "That could take a minute. If you stay with me, I can let you have this one or buy you one tomorrow. What you think about that?"

I opened my purse and looked inside so he could see the thick wads of cash that I'd made from dancing the night before. I then pulled out my car keys and held them in my hand. "What I think is I still got more work to do, so I can pay for my education. If you ain't gon' give me no money for that, then don't waste yo money."

Dominic stood there watching as I left the porch and got into *my* car. He was still trying to lure me back by going overboard with showing off whenever he was around me. I never gave in to the foolishness. I'd just laugh at his tactics, give him my son and keep it moving. He was hurt as fuck about not being able to lure me back in, not even when he'd bought a Cadillac. They were everything to me, and were the only brand of cars my mama would buy. His pressed ass had the nerve to go out and buy a Cadillac truck just to try to get me back. Yet again, the shit didn't work. I wasn't fazed one bit. It wasn't because I didn't love Dominic, but I was too far over his games. Also, I was too busy doing my own thing and I didn't plan on stopping a damn thing to go back to a controlling and insecure man.

At the time, I was casually dating and enjoying every moment of it. Not one person could say I was tied down to them on a serious matter, and that's the way I preferred it to be. That was until I ran into a DJ who drove me insane. He'd had a weird obsession with me and refused to give me my space.

First of all, he had a woman, but was always sniffing behind me, talking about he was going to leave her for me. I didn't believe that shit for one minute, and definitely wasn't waiting for it to happen. He was my nigga, though, and paid for whatever I needed. From clothes, to getting my hair and nails done . . . he'd give me anything I wanted. The money I made was used to pay for school and my son. But just like so many other men, he wanted to control me. As we sat in his car one day, I made it clear to him that I wasn't traveling down that road again.

"Listen, man. You can't have a whole woman out here and still be trying to put rules and regulations on me. You can't give me stipulations when you're going home to another woman every night. That don't work for me."

"What do my woman got to do with anything? This about you and me, nothing else. I don't like all those other niggas trying to get at you. You need to tell them to fall back, and why you gotta flirt and tease them muthafuckas all the time."

I blew off his comments and touched the doorknob so I could exit his car. "I'ma keep doing my job, and you need to stay doing yours. All this controlling shit don't work for me. If you wanna keep seeing me, you gon' have to chill the hell out with making demands."

I exited the car, and he didn't call me for two days. After that, the nigga came to where I was at my sister's house to drop off money for my car note. He apologized for trying to control me, and I quickly learned that whenever a woman stood her ground and put a stop to certain shit, she always came out a winner.

He walked into her house, telling me he was there to drop off the money, while I was downstairs keekeeing and joking with my sister's boyfriend and his friends. She had let him in and I was shocked to see him standing there with an attitude.

"Do you think we can step outside and holla for a minute?" he asked. "I need some privacy and too many niggas down here."

We went outside to talk, but he started the same bullshit again.

"Why the fuck you downstairs around all those niggas?"

I cut my eyes at him while he paced back and forth in front of his car.

"Not that it matters, but I grew up with all of those guys in there. I don't even have to answer to you, but what the fuck you want me to do? Leave when they come around 'cause you don't like it?"

He stopped pacing and looked at me through evil eyes. "You shoulda stayed upstairs in another room. Ain't no need for you to be downstairs with all those niggas."

I was so done with him. He just didn't know it yet. "What the fuck type of sense is you making right now? I'm not staying in no damn room because of your insecurities. Especially, when you going home to your woman."

"She ain't my woman. I told you I'm getting out of that situation."

"Getting out of a situation and being out of a situation are two different things. So, until you get outta that situation and come to me, you don't get to tell me what I can and cannot do. Point blank. And always remember that what you won't do, somebody else will!"

He stomped back to his car like a bitch and drove the fuck off, without giving me my car note money. I didn't give a fuck. I wasn't begging no nigga for nothing; I was quickly learning how some of them muthafuckas operated. Pay the fuck attention. It was one of the last times I ever spoke to his raggedy ass and that was fine with me. At that point, I didn't have time for shit like that. My motto was I only slept with one nigga at a time, but I always had a couple lined up and prepped. So, that little stunt didn't stop anything except me talking to him, period. And when I showed him who really had the upper hand, you'd better believe he kept trying to come back and apologize. I told him, "If you ain't leaving her, then I don't wanna hear it. Don't call my phone no more."

I'd meant what I'd said, and my sister was proud of me for standing my ground. The two of us had started hanging together. She was eight years older than me, but her man was my age, so all his friends that were my age, too, hung out at her crib. I'd grown up with all of them. Probably half of them liked me, but their money wasn't long enough, so I didn't pay them no mind. Mr. DJ just didn't know how innocent me being around those guys was, but I wasted no time trying to calm his insecurities and give into his demands.

After that incident, and while Dominic still hadn't been arrested yet, I hit him up once or twice for my car note money. He was waiting for that moment to come and boasted during dinner at a restaurant about me still needing him.

"You know I ain't got nothing but money to help you when I want to, but what happened to all those dollars you had falling outta yo purse? You spent that shit already?"

"Yep, and now that I'm on my own, I have hella more bills to pay. I don't need to hear a lecture from you, either you gon' give me the money or not."

He chewed his food while staring at me. A few minutes later, he went into his wallet and dropped the money on the table. "Whether you know it or not, I still got yo back," he said. "You just need to have mine more often, too."

Like I'd said before, there were times when I'd had his back more than I'd had my own. I took the money without any hesitation, and any time I fell short of money, I always went back to Dominic. For a second, we were back talking, though we never really had sex again. We'd go out with my son and spend time together like that, but the connection I'd once had with Dominic just wasn't there anymore. He was still looking at me like some little girl he could control. But I was so far from that little girl, and was learning how to be my own boss. I was starting to discover how powerful I was. Sometimes, I could tell a nigga to do something and he would just do it. Not that Dominic wasn't like that for me, but around him I felt like a little girl. I was becoming this woman, this boss, but being in his presence made me feel like he was one of my parents. I'd always be forced to revert back to being a kid when I was around him. I didn't like that feeling. I couldn't have that, and I had to unleash the new me.

Chapter Nine

Back into the groove of things, I was now at the point where I was single and needed to keep money afloat while out on my own. I had been dancing for close to a year and was at a point in my exotic dance career where I would book private parties for some of my supporters who frequented the club. Dominic was no longer in the picture. He was locked up, so the only person I had outside of my family was Dallas. Of course, her crazy ass wasn't going nowhere. The two of us were stuck together like glue, and any crazy idea she had in mind, I had no choice but to see that shit through as her best friend. Just like the time she moved out of the home she shared with her boyfriend, while he was at work. I helped her pack that day, and was completely exhausted as we piled her car with her belongings. She also had a U-Haul truck in front of the house. It was filled to capacity as well, and the dude driving it was a nigga she had been messing with.

"That nigga gon' miss me when I'm gone!" She wiped sweat from her forehead and fanned herself with her hand. It must've been 100 plus degrees outside that day, and I was just ready to go before Ace got home and started clowning.

"I don't think you gonna fit anything else in this car, so let's go. If you left something, come back and get it another day."

Dallas ignored me and stood there in a daze, biting her bottom lip. Then, she snapped her fingers, remembering that she needed to go back into the house to get one more thing.

"I can't leave my makeup brushes inside. They cost too much, and I know that nigga gon' throw away anything I leave. And what about my boots? I can't believe I left my boots in the fucking closet!"

She raced towards the house and went outside. Frustrated, I leaned against the car, drinking the last swig of water I'd had in a cup. I was thirsty and hungry. Dallas needed to hurry up, and when she came back outside, she had about ten more items we had to somehow stuff into her car.

"I don't have nowhere to sit," I said. "Please tell me where in the hell am I going to sit in this car."

Dallas rushed to the passenger's side of the car and tried to squeeze me inside. We laughed our asses off as she attempted to shut the door and it wouldn't close. Seeing her laugh at that moment meant everything to me, and I knew she was frustrated about what her and Ace had been going through. When all was said and done, she left that day, only to move right back in with Ace the very next day. That's just how crazy Dallas was, but I had no choice but to love her crazy ass for being her, and for always being there for me. Shortly after moving back home, she and Ace went away to elope without even telling anyone. I thought it was the funniest shit in the world. Meanwhile, I was tied down to not one nigga, while living my best life. That was a fact.

While dancing one night, I met a guy from down river who went by the name of JP. JP and the Packer Boyz were well known throughout the city, especially from down river because of the type of business they were into like big-time drug dealing. Per usual, all the bitches loved them some JP. I recognized him and his boys from seeing them around town when I was out and about, dancing or partying at clubs. They always rolled deep together, and everybody knew not to fuck with them. They had that kind of rep in the streets and no one could deny it.

JP was at a birthday party for one of his boys. Me and a few of the other strippers I'd worked with were paid and booked to entertain the entire party. I was thankful as hell for JP and his conversation, because not one time during the whole night did I have to dance or entertain anyone other than him. We sat around talking all night. That's all he wanted from me that night.

"Just sit yo pretty self-down in that chair over there and talk to me," he said in such a smooth, relaxing voice. "Sometimes, I just like to talk to people to see where their head at. Especially people I have interest in."

JP wasn't really a pretty boy type, but he was still easy on the eyes. He also had mad sex appeal, and with beautiful brown skin, the smoothest voice I had ever heard, and a shiny bald head, he definitely had my attention. I loved how he towered over my small frame and gazed into my eyes like something serious was on his mind.

"Why do you even want to get into my head?" I asked, before taking a seat. "Wouldn't you rather be out there partying with yo friends?"

The way he narrowed his eyes and glared at me, I could tell he was more than interested. But that night, he was determined to penetrate my mind and find out more about me.

"Tell me how you got into doing this shit. I bet you a thousand dollars that you got one hell of a story to tell. There seems to be so much mystery behind who you are, and word on the street is you got it going on."

I laughed, kicked off my heels and crossed my legs. Feeling very comfortable around him, I was relaxed. "The streets don't lie, then again, sometimes they do because nobody ever told me you were this nice. Before I tell you about me, I wanna know what's up with you. How did you get in the game or why did you choose to?"

JP and I engaged in an interesting conversation all night that revolved around our lives and the choices we'd made. He kept me laughing. He kept me guessing. He kept me on my toes. I wasn't too pressed to dance that night either because he paid how he weighed just for me to sit there with him. I respected that he knew exactly how the game worked. He knew even though I liked him that time was money—always would be—and he didn't hesitate to pay a bitch for her time. He had already earned my respect, and to top it off, that nigga had swag out this world. He was highly intelligent, but like so many other niggas, he was married to the streets. That alone caused a dent in our relationship, before it even had the chance to fully take off.

When we started dating, there would be times he'd call to say he was on his way. I'd wake up the next morning realizing I'd fallen asleep in my clothes while waiting on him to pick me up. Never in my mind did I think he'd tell me he was on his way, and then go pick up another bitch. But I didn't put anything past no nigga. JP, however, was as genuine as they came. There was no doubt in my mind that he was out dealing street business. There would even be times he'd scoop me up, and while en route to our destination, his phone would start blowing up and we'd get rerouted for the whole entire day. We'd be in the car for hours at a time, while he rode around making his money. And don't get me wrong . . . I wasn't the type of woman to come in between a hustler and his money. There was just never a time he didn't put the streets first. I tried to deal with it for as long as I could, because outside of his street dealings, I found myself liking JP a lot. Not only was he charming as hell, but he wined and dined me just like Dominic had done. So honestly, it was easy for me to "fall in like" with him.

JP also taught me some new shit that I wasn't used to. I'd hit my first blunt with him, and he taught me how the weed game worked. For a while, that became one of my side hustles. From there, shit was up. We would get so damn high that we would find ourselves having passionate, heated sex for hours at a time.

"Turn that ass over, girl, and let me hit that shit like I want to," he said.

We were lying on the bed in his bedroom, and had fucked our way to the floor. As he requested, I got into position on my hands and knees. He positioned his dick at the crevasses of my wet folds, and after teasing me for a while, he drove all nine inches of his meat inside of me. He delivered long strokes that made my knees buckle. I moaned, while letting him know how much his performance felt superior to me.

"Do that shit, nigga! You know how to make a bitch feel good, and this—this dick is doing the daaaaaamn thing!"

Whenever I applauded the nigga's efforts, the shit just got better and better. I got a real thrill out of fucking him, and it wasn't no surprise when I got pregnant. I told him the news while he was riding around making drops one day.

"Damn," he said, looking at me in shock. "I'm really about to be somebody's daddy. That shit funny as hell. And in other words, you gon' be my baby's mama."

"Yep and a whole lot more than that. I got a feeling that you gon' be a good daddy too."

JP smiled and reached out to give me a hug. He was happy as hell; it was the cutest thing in the world to me. Deep down, though, I was hella concerned. I'd already had one son who was five years old now, and bringing another child into this world would be a challenge for me. I'd vowed to never have another abortion, so that wasn't an option. I just had to make the best of my situation, and JP seemed like he'd be a good dad.

DETROIT MADAM

During my pregnancy, I danced all the way up until I was four months just to stack up a few extra dollars. I was still enrolled in school, but shortly after JP found out about the baby, he ended up getting arrested on a drug possession charge. He served one year behind bars, but in the meantime, it left me pregnant with his baby and a five-year-old son to take care of. Our plans were shattered, and with no baby's father in sight, I ended up meeting a guy named Monte who had been coming to the club for about a year straight. Our first official encounter was for entertainment and business purposes. Monte was ten years older than me and he'd had his shit all the way together. He had a successful home improvement company, and did some hustling on the side. He always dressed nice, wore Coogi sweaters, rocked a bald head, and was very clean-cut. No 'gaters or Tims, but somewhere in between. Needless to say, he was real grown with his shit, and walked around smelling good. We'd been chit-chatting with each other here and there, and he finally got the courage to ask me out on a date. Being pregnant, I wasn't sure if I wanted to go, but when I told Monte about my pregnancy, he still wanted to go out. Dating lasted for a while, and we'd waited a few months before deciding to have sex. He was *different* for sure, and I was happy about him becoming a father figure to my kids. Outside of him being a blessing to my kids, he was financially a blessing to me as well. If he didn't do nothing else, he taught me how to fucking chase a bag. For that, I was forever grateful.

To this day, he calls me baby girl, and that's how he always looked at me. He always made everything about me. I needed that at the time, and even though he was all about his money, he still made time to take care of me. I considered him a blessing, because later on down the road, he was the key to opening the door to everything. It was Kandi's Dazzling Entertainment, a business that made me some of the most money I'd ever made in my fucking life.

Chapter Ten

January 2001. A chill had swept across the city of Detroit, heavy snow had fallen and the new millennium was in full swing. I had officially given birth to a beautiful baby girl, and was now the mother of two amazing little brown kids. Dominic and JP were in jail. My sister had two boys and my brother was the father of a set of twin boys. Imagine how my having the first girl changed our worlds. There was so much excitement in my family. Simply put, shit was lit! Monte continued to step up to the plate while JP was in jail. He was more than a great provider; to say I was living a good life with him would be an understatement. I didn't have to worry about anything bill-wise, and he never complained about getting up for work every day. He was a man's man who took care of what was his and always had his ear to the streets. Things were going so well that I was able to stay home with the kids for three months, after my daughter was born. That was the positive side, but on the flipside, Monte drank a lot. He'd fuck up a whole bottle of Hennessey within an hour, and over time his drinking had escalated. At first, I didn't notice how bad his drinking habit was. I just knew that more and more often, he was coming home drunk.

"Please don't tell me you drunk again," I said, as he stumbled into the bedroom. The smell of alcohol was strong as hell, and the closer he got to me, I could smell it on his breath. With a glassy film covering his eyes, he puckered for a kiss.

"I'm not drunk, just tipsy. Gimmie a kizzz," he slurred.

I rolled my eyes and tended to my beautiful baby in my arms, while giving her some milk. Monte plopped on the bed and fell back. As he stared at the ceiling, I reminded him how much his drinking was getting out of control.

"I can see you doing this shit every once in a while, but every damn day, Monte? You gotta come in here drunk every day, and didn't you promise me you would chill out?"

He massaged his forehead and slowly sat up. "I tried, baby, but a nigga need a little something to relax him sometimes. Besides, my drinking ain't bothering nobody. I—"

Before he could say another way, he belched and vomited right on the floor beside the bed. I was furious, especially when he passed out a few minutes after that. I couldn't take care of no drunk ass nigga and my babies at the same time. Realizing that this wasn't going to work out with us much longer, and because I was used to having my own shit, I went right back to dancing. My daughter was three-and-a half months, and I couldn't sit around waiting for an unpredictable drunk to get it together. The house mama life, while a dream for some, was boring as hell to me. I needed to get up and get out. I needed my own time away and my own money in my pocket. That had been one of my priorities, and you'd better believe that I bounced back really quick.

One of the reasons I'd stayed with Dominic as long as I had was because I felt indebted to him. I had started to feel indebted to Monte, too. Having that feeling ate me alive, and I always felt like I needed to do something to escape it. Here was this man taking care of kids who weren't even his. But I couldn't get with it, because at the end of the day, I needed to be confident in my ability to take care of my kids on my own. I needed to know that if he ever walked away or didn't want to do something for my kids, we'd still be okay; I'd still be able to provide for them. I tried to explain that to Monte, but he kept telling me that he didn't mind taking care of us.

"I got you," he said. "You don't need to start working again, and stressing yourself out. I can handle this and taking care of yo kids ain't no problem for me."

"I appreciate you, Monte, but it's a problem for me. I don't know how to say this, but you doing too much. If I let you do everything, what's gon' happen when you just up and leave? I can't put myself in no position like that."

"Leave? I already told you that I ain't going nowhere. Why can't you get that through yo thick head?"

I laughed, but did what I had to do. That consisted of going back to work. "You say you'll never leave, but my thick head is smart enough to know that men say one thing and do another. I gotta make sure my kids are taken care of forever. That ain't on you. That's on me."

Monte kept trying to convince me that he'd be there forever. And after a while, his words went in one ear, out the other. There was no way for me to tell him he'd better do this or that for me or my kids. And while some women were okay with shit like a man doing everything, I wasn't. I needed to be secure on my own.

DETROIT MADAM

As quickly as I got back into that dancing lifestyle, I was just as quick to make my official exit all over again. Shit was just played out. One day, I had just stopped dancing in the middle of the floor and looked around at how this business was run. Mostly greedy ass men were in control. They didn't give a damn about none of the girls who worked at their clubs. I realized that I didn't need to be paying any club owners my money in tip outs to dance at their establishments. Once I knew the game, I knew that I could do this shit and make either equal money or more, without owing the clubs I worked at a single fucking penny. I kept reminding myself how much I knew the game. How I had done this shit before, with the help of Dominic. How I knew so many people, particularly clients, who would support my new endeavors. So why was I continuing to show up every night and give somebody else my money? What in the hell was the purpose?

Night after night, I got tired of asking myself the same questions. I remembered how I'd felt when I was dancing before I'd had my daughter. I felt like these muthafuckas were double dipping because they were charging us girls to dance, charging guests to get in to the club, and on top of that, they were getting paid hella money from the bar. It was major overkill, and I wasn't with people taking advantage of me anymore. Not to mention, I would go do parties and there would be so many girls there working to put food on their tables. These assholes paid us scraps; I was starting to see less and less money in the entertainment world. Crazy as it sounded though, I knew it was more money out there to be made. I just had to figure out a way to do and shake some shit up in Detroit. Needing some extra cash to get things started, I went to Monte with the idea and pitched it to him. It was just me and him at a pool hall that day. He was slightly drunk, and a cigarette dangled from the corner of his mouth, as he leaned over the pool table about to shoot.

"So, that's my idea and this is what I need from you," I said. "I need the startup money to strike it out on my own."

"I heard yo idea, but if you ask me, it's real ambitious. Then you got all these niggas out here trying to run the same game. How can you compete with that shit?"

He struck the ball with the pool stick and made his shot. Before he took another one, I needed his full attention so I walked up to him and took the stick from his hand.

"Listen, Monte. I ain't saying this shit gon' be easy, but you gotta trust me on this. I know my way around and I visualize how everything can work. Besides, I don't mind the competition. That don't stop me, and you know how when I get this shit in my head, how determined I am. Just help me, alright?"

Monte took a hit from the cigarette, and then blew smoke into the air. He pondered hard while staring at me.

"I guess if anybody can do this, you can. I'll front you the money, and all I ask is that you handle yo shit well and let them niggas know who the real boss is around here."

I smiled and held out my pinky finger. "Bet. Just sit back and watch me do my thing. I may even get to a point where I'll be taking care of you."

This time he laughed and shook his head. "That will never happen. I'm a hardworking man and ain't no women ever gon' have to take care of me."

I predicted that I wouldn't have to, but was grateful to Monte for believing in my ideas and giving me the money. He was my partner. We needed the money to get the DBA for our entertainment business, to get business cards made and I had to get a business line set up in the house. That didn't even include advertisements around Detroit that took up the bulk of the money. The rest of it was spent on supplies I needed to get my home office up and running. Before I knew it, Dazzle 'em Entertainment came to fruition.

Before the name Dazzle 'em was set in stone, we started finding girls from all over Detroit to come work for us. We found the girls just like we'd found our male clients: by advertising in the back of popular publications like *The Metro Times*. And good ole fashioned pounding the pavement always worked. We handed out business cards to women who looked like they could dance and men who looked like they could pay. A lot of them who ended up on our payroll were girls I already knew and had worked in the strip club with me.

With Dazzle 'em, we would send girls out on call requests for one-on-one sessions. A man might call in and say he was looking for a girl to come spend a couple hours with him, to dance for him. We'd match him with the person who fit his needs and send her out. As a safety measure, Monte would drive girls to their destinations and wait for them to come out. If we had multiple women out at once, everyone would pile in Monte's vehicle at the same time. We even set up a call process for them to call us immediately, if there was an emergency. We wanted to protect our girls at all cost, and luckily for us, we never had anyone call us to say there was an emergency. Our shit was so legit; it took off fast as fuck. There were all different kinds of guys contacting us for their nightly entertainment. The phone was ringing off the hook and I could barely keep up. Whether I sat there with rollers in my hair and my nightgown on, or in business attire that I sometimes wore, I did my best to keep shit moving.

"Thank you for calling Dazzle 'em entertainment," I said in a very sexy, seductive and professional voice. "How may I assist you today?"

"Hello. My name is Steve and I'm having a birthday party in two weeks. A good friend of mine told me about two girls that came to his party. He said that shit was lit. Can you tell me how I can get the girls to come to my party? I think it'll be fun and I'm expecting about thirty or forty people, maybe more."

"Well, Steve, what I can do is promise you and your friends a good time. You mentioned two girls, but with that many people, I'm not sure if two will be enough. Tell me how many hours you would like to book the girls for, what is your location and who, specifically, told you about us? We like to give discounts to some of our clients who rave about our services. We'll be happy to do the same for you, and we do hope that you'll contact us again, every time you have a party."

Steve and I laughed and talked like we'd known each other for years. I had mastered how to engage with my clients on a professional level, and they truly appreciated my efforts to be *different*.

With Dazzle 'em Entertainment, the client paid the girl directly when she showed up. I would do a 40/60 split with the girl, for her to entertain the client for the night or for however many hours they'd requested. Now, I'll say this, for business purposes it was strictly about dancing and entertainment. Whatever bitches chose to do to get a little extra coin was simply on them, but in my eyes, as a business owner, it was all about dancing and that only. As long as the girls didn't provide any extras, any sexual services, which we had no control over, our business was completely legal. Nonetheless, I was nobody's fool and I wasn't trying to convince anybody to be one. I'd heard all type of shit that bitches were doing while on a job, from tricking to fucking to sucking to eating . . . to whatever you could think of. But, as long as shit didn't include me or tamper with my business, I really didn't question it. I made everything perfectly clear in the contracts I had everybody I did business with sign. Many didn't hesitate.

"Read this over and sign at the bottom," I said to a new girl who was trying to make some extra paper while putting herself through school. She reminded me so much of myself. I definitely understood her struggles.

"I read it, but are you sure I don't have to engage in sex with anybody, unless I want to? I just wanna be sure, because all I wanna do is dance. I've been dancing since I was a kid. And even though this is a different type of dancing, I know I can do it."

"I saw you do your thing at another club and you do have skills. If not, I wouldn't have reached out to you. And yes, all you gotta do is dance. It's up to you if you choose to do anything else, but please do not tell me about anything extra that you do. I don't wanna know, and it ain't my business. Just make as much money as you can to help with school, and as you read in the contract, you are not obligated to stay hooked up with my company."

"That's good to know. And I thank you, Kandi, for being so sweet and giving me this opportunity. I don't think some people understand how we women just gotta do what we gotta do to make ends meet. It's rough out there, and with a kid to take care of, I gotta do something."

"I feel you on that, and you can trust me when I tell you I wholeheartedly understand."

That day, Sylvia signed the contract and had quickly worked her way to the top of our requested dancer's list. I didn't know what she was doing to stay so popular, and it didn't make no difference to me, as long as I was getting to the bag. That's all I cared about, honestly. During that period, I didn't even notice that I was on the verge of building a reputation as a madam—a provider of superior female entertainment. But I had my eyes on the fucking prize and was willing to do whatever was necessary to get that company off the ground, put some money in my girls' pockets and live a good life. I was done with dancing, unless I wanted to do it. This was a whole new avenue.

After a short while, nearly every guy from Detroit that was a club goer wanted to work with me or get females for their entertainment through my company. It got to the point where it was damn near as if the city had said fuck the strip clubs. Monte couldn't believe it, and he came into the office to give me big props one day. A bouquet of flowers was in his hands, but unfortunately, the stench of alcohol was all on his breath.

"Deep down," he said, handing me the flowers. "I always knew you would make this business blow the hell up. I just didn't expect it to be like this. I've been driving all around this city, dropping the girls off and making niggas real happy. Not to mention all the money we done made."

I sniffed the beautiful bouquet of flowers, then laid them on my desk. I wanted to be so happy about everything, but Monte's drinking habits were a big problem for us. I seriously thought he'd get into an accident while driving some of the girls around. He was always passing out, and the kids seeing him like that all the time wasn't good.

"The money is definitely good, and thanks for the flowers. I told you we were on to something, didn't I?"

He nodded and then diverted our conversation elsewhere. "I noticed that some of those niggas been asking for you to come dance for them. I hope you ain't doing no shit on the side to make extra money. That wouldn't sit right with me. It would be like a betrayal, when we supposed to be in this together."

I was taken aback by his comment. He was on some bullshit; I guess it was the only thing he could use to divert from his drinking situation that drove me nuts.

"Monte, I don't have time to entertain your foolishness." The phone rang and prevented me from going off on him like I wanted to. "I have a business to run, and if you like the kind of money we making like you say you do, then I suggest you put the bottle down and rethink that bullshit you just said to me."

I cut my eyes at him and picked up the phone to take the call. Business was my main priority, outside of my kids. Monte kept on clowning on me about dumb shit, and his drinking had picked up like crazy. His insecurities had gone overboard. It was beginning to become unmanageable between my relationship and my coin. Most of the guys who would come through our company would request me, but because it was about business first and foremost, I would rarely ever go out on the call, unless I chose to. If I did, it was because one of my girls didn't show up or scheduling issues occurred. But men requesting me fucked with his head. It also gave him just another reason to drink. My biggest concern became his drunk ass transporting the girls to and from locations. I wanted to make sure they were okay at all times. Even when I confronted him about it, he tried to make it all about me.

"The only reason you so invested in this shit is so you can go fuck them other niggas." He was so mad; spit was flying from his mouth. This type of nonsense was ruining everything, including our partnership, right before my eyes.

All I would say with the phone up to my ear, while booking parties was, "Monte, not to-fucking-day, okay?"

That's all I could say because I was tired of hearing it and seeing him drunk. My head would be banging from constant headaches. If he saw a nigga call my phone more than once, he would keep a mental note of it and use it against me in the midst of one of his drunken episodes. Liquor had won over this nigga, and it was getting in the way of this big ass bag we were building. Some of my clients would hear him cussing and fussing in the background. It was not only embarrassing, but heartbreaking as well. In order to stay afloat, I had a critical decision to make. The conclusion was, Monte and I needed to depart. My problem was how I would go about telling him this partnership was a wrap.

Chapter Eleven

My plans to tell Monte I was moving on was harder than I thought it would be. I prolonged the conversation, and then I recalled a conversation Dallas and I had on the phone about me running into my son's father while I was out and about shopping. I'd seen him as I was coming out of a store. I'd spoken to him, but I really didn't have much else to say to him. He didn't want to be in his son's life, unless me and him were together. I didn't want to be with him, which, to me, meant he didn't want to be around his son. So, it was hi, what's up . . . how you doing and then bye. After that, I got in my car and left. I'd told Dallas about the brief encounter over the phone. She let me know exactly how she felt.

"You should've slapped the shit outta him. I can't stand niggas who don't take care of their kids, and whether you with him or not, his ass should've stepped up to the plate a long time ago."

"Girl, I wouldn't waste no time or energy slapping that fool. His stupid ass tried to be nice, and he had the audacity to come at me like I would really wanna be with him."

"Well, if he thinks that, his ass is delusional. I can't believe he ain't offer you nothing or even ask if he could stop by to see his son."

"Nope, he didn't say one word, and he damn sure didn't offer me any money. Regardless, I'm done talking about him. I need to clean up a little, before Monte gets here. You know him and me need to have a little talk."

"Yeah, well, good luck with that conversation. Go ahead and tell that nigga how you feel about everything. Better now, than later."

I agreed, and while I was vacuuming the floors, Monte came in. He was swaying back and forth like he was dizzy. Eyes were fire red and a brown paper bag with a liquor bottle inside was clenched in his hand. I was so disgusted with him, and at first glance, I knew a civil conversation wasn't going to happen. Maybe by morning he'd be sober enough to talk.

"Aye," he said, wobbling while trying to stand up straight. "We got something in there to eat?"

I shrugged and turned off the vacuum cleaner. "I don't know what's in there. Why don't you go look?"

He barely made it down the hallway and had to use the walls to hold himself up. I put the vacuum cleaner away and went into the bedroom to get my bath clothes ready. After my bath, while I was sitting on the edge of the bed, Monte came into the room with a glass in his hand. Dark brown liquid was in it, so I already knew what it was.

"I had a dream you ran into yo baby daddy," he said, bluntly.

I frowned and twisted my face. His words caught me off guard. "What? Why would you dream about something like that?"

He shrugged his shoulders, before lying on the bed. The smell on his breath made me sick to my fucking stomach. I could never get used to his smell.

"Yeaaaaah," he slurred. "I had a dream you ran into him, and that nigga was trying to tap into my pussy."

"Monte, please," I said, waving him off while rubbing lotion on my legs. "Don't nobody got time for this drunk-ass shit tonight."

Now, I'd waved him off like I didn't give a hoot, but I was thinking . . . *Damn, this nigga good as fuck. I did see that nigga. How did he know?*

Then, it hit me. I noticed that every time I picked up my phone, I would always hear a click or some weird noise. My mind immediately went to some TV crime drama mystery, and I always thought it was the feds trying to make sure I wasn't doing no illegal mess. Not that I would talk about illegal business on the phone anyway, but I preferred to keep my calls clean, until I figured out what that noise was. Monte left me alone that night, but a few nights later I caught his ass in the act. He was drunk out of his fucking mind, only this time, he thought I was sleep. I wasn't and I tiptoed behind him as he turned the lights on and crept into the basement. At first, I didn't know what to expect, especially when I'd heard a female's voice coming from the basement. I charged forward and hurried down the stairs thinking, *I know this nigga ain't bring no bitch up in my house!*

That would've been an epic violation like, "You 'bout to get fucked up just on GP!" The voice got louder, and by the time I reached the bottom stair, I was heated. I was ready to attack both him and the bitch who was brave enough to come into my home, but as soon as I turned in his direction, I saw his goofy ass sitting in a chair while listening to a conversation I'd had on the phone earlier. This fool was listening to me on a recorder! I was just as livid as I would've been, if he'd actually had another bitch in the house.

"Are you fucking kidding me?" I screamed at the top of my lungs.

Startled as fuck, Monte jumped from the chair and stood in front of me. He towered over my short frame, but I was all up in his face, going off on him for doing this.

"I—I wanted to make sure you wasn't doing nothing you ain't have no business doing with these niggas," he stuttered. He knew his ass was busted. There was no justification for recording my conversations. I didn't know how many more recorders there were, and I wondered if he had hidden them all around the house.

"This is fucking ridiculous," I said, stomping away from him. I went from room to room, looking for more recorders. I was hardly ever in the basement, other than to do laundry, so without this incident I would have probably never realized that he was spying on me. I questioned how long the shit had been going on, but Monte didn't have much to say. I figured the whole time we'd been together he had tapped my phone and was on some real-life stalking shit. All the phone clicking I'd heard was due to him. He knew I'd seen my son's father because he'd heard me tell Dallas all about it.

Monte kept apologizing like his life depended on it. He begged me not to do anything drastic, but he couldn't even defend himself because he was so damn drunk.

"I just love you sooooo much," he whined. "And I needed to make sure none of those niggas could get to you."

I rejected that bullshit and kept screaming in his face. "Love me? Nigga is this what love is! You running yo ass up in here drunk all the time, recording me and shit, and then accusing me of fucking around! This shit ain't love. I'm done with this. I don't want nothing else to do with you!"

As I walked away, Monte grabbed my arm and spun me around to face him. I had never witnessed him be so aggressive; the look in his eyes was deadly.

"You think you gon' just up and walk away from me, after all the shit I than done for you? Yo ass ain't going nowhere!"

"Let me go!" I tried to pull away from him, and demanded that he get the hell out. To my surprise, he took shit to a whole new level, when he pushed me away from him. I stumbled backwards, and watched as he reached in his pants and pulled out a gun. He aimed it at me with tears streaming down his face. I stared without a blink and stood like cement had been poured over me. Everything around me stood still.

"I'm just going to end this!" he shouted. "If we can't be together, you right, this shit is over!"

In that moment, I didn't think there was no happy ending to this situation. Monte was very emotional while waving the gun around and rambling on and on about our relationship. The only thing I could do was try to calm him down.

"Monte, you don't want to do this," I said, panicking. "What are you about to end? We still got so much to live for, and I know you don't want to go out like this."

I was in complete disbelief that he'd pulled a gun on me. Just that fast the tables had turned again. All I could think about was the gun in his hand and my babies upstairs, especially when he paused again to aim the gun at my head. He was sweating all over and spoke through gritted teeth.

"I'm about to put an end to me and you! Both of us! If I can't have you, if we can't be together, then fuck it!"

A single tear rolled down my face as I stood thinking it would all end here. I didn't ever need a nigga to love me this fucking much, and nothing ever good came from this kind of *love*. Unfortunately, I could've never predicted this. Not Monte . . . my own man, the father figure to my kids, the man who had helped me build this business—I just couldn't believe it. I couldn't even think straight, and when a bullet from his gun whizzed through the air, my emotions ran over. I fell to my knees, feeling so lucky that he'd shot the bullet into the ceiling. White powder rained down from the bullet hole, and when I looked up to see it, I screamed and scrambled off the floor as fast as I could.

"My babies!"

Like a bat out of hell, I rushed up the stairs to go make sure they were okay. Thank God they were, and after checking on them, I dropped to my knees in the hallway. With smudged mascara stained on my face, I clenched my hands together and started to thank God. I didn't know if Monte had left or not, but what he'd done was a slap in my face. It woke me up immediately. Instantly. Eventually, it woke him up as well. I could have lost my life because of his stupid shit. One of my kids could have lost theirs. He could've harmed himself—the shit wasn't even worth it. It was easy to tell him he had to go, but those words put me in such an awkward position because Monte didn't have anywhere to go. He was giving me all his money, and he wasn't one of those men who had a secret stash of cash that I didn't know about. I knew where all of his money was. We had been living off of it. We were living comfortably, but not so comfortably that we had thousands just sitting in a savings account at a bank. A lot of our money had been used to manage and promote Dazzle 'em

Entertainment, and the bulk of his money went into our household. There was no way he would leave the house, so I left instead.

That moment was the deciding factor for me that broke our relationship. It was more than enough for me to walk away. Shit could have been so amazing between the two of us, because outside of alcohol and insecurities, he was more than a decent man. At that time, being decent wasn't enough. There were only so many chances I could give a grown man to kink out his flaws. I got sick of preaching, and Monte just didn't want to get his act together. I wasn't about to risk my damn life, again, nor the lives of my kids.

After that incident, I headed to my stepmom's house. I stayed there for a few days, but after numerous conversations with Monte about his actions, he had a sobering moment and admitted to his wrongdoings. He decided to move out of our house, and days later, Dallas moved in. She helped me out a lot, and since she'd been having an up-and-down relationship with Ace, I was able to help her out, too. The timing was perfect because she needed somewhere to stay. As for Monte, he vowed to always, no matter what, remain there for me and my kids. It was a promise he'd kept, and to this day, he continues to keep his word. The end of our relationship, though, ended our partnership with Dazzle 'em Entertainment. I didn't want him to be able to say I'd stood on his back to get where I was or to claim he had any stake in the money the business was making, so I left that business behind to start a new one. I turned everything from Dazzle 'em Entertainment over to him. He could run it on his own, if he wanted to. But he never did anything with it. That business just died right there.

I started my own entertainment company, Kandi's Dazzling Entertainment, with brand new everything, courtesy of the help I received from Dallas. At that point, the Detroit Madam was officially born.

Because I'd known at least half of the men in the city who made money from sending out girls through Dazzle 'em, the very minute word got out about Kandi's Dazzling Entertainment, females from all over came to dance and work under my company. We didn't even do ads in the paper this time. A lot of it was word of mouth and, once again, hitting the pavement. My goal was to always keep a low profile, no matter what. My mother still lived in the city, and the last thing I wanted to do was allow shit to get back to her. That would have been a whole different can of worms I wouldn't have been able to contain. During this time, I still kept little temp jobs off and on, so when money got slow or I didn't have anything to do during the week, I was set. My mama knew about my temp jobs, and she knew, of course, that I'd danced in the past. But she never knew the extent to which these parties were blowing up. She thought I was just temping. After she'd cursed me out about dancing a couple years prior, I could never be honest with her about what I was actually doing. She worked in the corporate world. Many people knew her around the way in that capacity, so I also didn't want to put a shadow on her name by associating her with my business in any way. I needed to be respectful of that, and was very careful not to enlist anyone she might have known. Some of the girls I'd known from working in clubs with them. But a lot of females also came from Dallas and I passing out cards to women we just happened to cross paths with. We would see girls dancing on the top of their cars at River Rouge Park, twerking for show and trying to be cute. Those were the ones we made offers to come work with us. On many summer nights in the D, River Rouge was the place to be. Ballers were out there driving around in their cars, flossing. Girls were dancing in the streets and on their cars to get niggas' attention and numbers. I would pull them aside and talk to them one by one.

"Girl, you out here doing this shit for attention," I said, being honest with one chick who was going hard for attention. "How about you get paid for what you doing? Come with us, and I'll show you how to make some for real money."

Sometimes, girls would gravitate towards me and my ladies when they saw us riding around together in decked out cars, looking fine as hell. They all naturally thought just like the one I was talking to did, as she examined my clothes, jewelry and the car I drove.

"Damn, if you got it like that, how can I get put on too? Tell me when and where to show up and I'm there."

She was down and thrilled to be a part of our team. Some chicks acted as if the shit was beneath them, and kept on putting on a show for niggas for free. However, the majority of their heads turned just as much as the men's did, when they saw us coming. It made it real easy to pick them up and take them on a ride to getting the bag with us. I'd give them my card and tell them I could show them the way.

"You wanna make money, I'll let you know when it's a party and you can come out and roll with us."

The business cards for Kandi's were the most rated X piece of promotions to ever touch the streets of Detroit. Some people still have those cards on deck—they were lit! I wore grey contacts on the card, while licking a lollipop with one hand and holding my exposed boob in the other hand. My hair was wet and curly. It was nothing but classic, and the cards had niggas going wild. I'd gotten so much business, period, and it had gotten to a point where muthafuckas didn't even give a care what my business cards looked like. I flicked it across the room and looked at Dallas who sat in a chair in front of me, counting money.

"Hey, if they don't give a fuck about those cards, neither do I. This shit is game on, girl, we doing the damn thing."

Dallas stood and placed a stack of money in front of me on the table. "You damn right we are. And you know what, sis? This shit is just the beginning!"

DETROIT MADAM

Chapter Twelve

Dallas was right about it being just the beginning. Business was picking up, but we still pounded the pavement to get even more. The goal was to be on top. Something inside wouldn't allow me to settle for anything less, so during the week, we continued to hustle like our lives depended on it. That meant passing out cards and flyers everywhere. We would stop at different gas stations to hand them out to people, and even post them on the walls inside. One night, Dallas was handing out business cards at a gas station and was bending over while talking to a guy through his window. Several other girls who had joined our team were sitting in the backseat of my car, waiting for the next person to pull up so they could share flyers with them. We were all focused on that, and not really paying much attention to our surroundings. As Dallas was talking to the dude in the car, trying to tell him he should book us for his next party, another car swerved behind his car and blocked him in. Not knowing what was going on, Dallas' head snapped up. I squinted to see what was going on as well. A Wesley Snipes looking nigga in a leather long jacket stepped out of the car with a shotgun underneath his jacket. That was all I needed to see, before I started yelling my head off.

"Girl, get in the fucking car! Hurry!"

Dallas had already started to make her move, but by then, the dude held up the shotgun and aimed it at her.

"Bitch, yo ass betta not move!"

It was a life or death situation, so Dallas made the only call she could make and sprinted to my car as fast as she could. The dude turned the gun on the driver of the car, demanding his money. By then, Dallas had dove into the front seat of my car, screaming like crazy.

"Pull off—drive off now!"

I had already put the gear in drive, while yelling for a few other girls to get their asses back in the car. Once everyone was inside, I skidded off the parking lot, burning rubber as I left. The thunderous roar of gunshots caused me to panic, and as another car that was speeding to get off the lot was in the way, that's when I realized one of my other girls wasn't even in the car. She had just run out the store, and had witnessed the robbery and shooting right in front of her.

"Run, bitch, run! Get the hell in the car and come on!" I said, waiting for her. She dove in the car, too, and refusing to wait around any longer, I swerved my car around another car, almost crashing into it. Every second it took us to get out of there, we knew we could've gotten shot and killed. I sped off, leaving tire marks on the pavement and a cloud of smoke behind me. My foot was on the pedal and pressed to the metal. I didn't stop the car until we were well out of sight from the gas station. And when we were, I pulled over on another parking lot, freaking out while my hands were trembling. I could barely catch my breath while looking at the girls who were a wreck like I was.

"I—I really couldn't see the gun as he was walking towards me," Dallas said, unable to catch her breath. "I—I didn't see anything until he told me b—bitch, don't move."

"I saw his gun and that's when I started yelling," I said. "This is so fucked up. Did it take all that to fucking rob somebody?"

"I know," Staci said tearfully. She was in the backseat crying her heart out and having a fit. "That muthafucka could've killed me. I saw him looking at me too. I just knew I was dead."

"Me too," Dallas added. "I was standing right fucking there!"

I wiped my tears and took several deep breaths to calm myself. "Lucky for us, we're okay. I feel bad for that nigga in that car. Did he get shot or did dude just rob him?"

"I saw him shoot in the air while yelling for the dude to give him his money and dope," Staci said. "Maybe he shot him after we left. I really don't know. I'm just glad to be the fuck away from there."

It was an overall messed up situation. And after things settled down, I realized we may have had a bigger problem on our hands. Detroit was notorious for running scams to set niggas up, where girls would set up a play for dudes to get robbed. Niggas knew how that game was played. Dallas had just given the guy our card, a few minutes before the nigga walked up to him and robbed him. He could have easily thought that we'd set him up. If he'd thought that, what would he do? Of course, he'd come looking for us for retaliation. I couldn't have that.

Right after that incident, we started doing thorough checks on every client we had coming in. We didn't know if the nigga was going to come back looking for Dallas or not, thinking she'd set him up when she didn't have anything to do with it. We started screening calls and asking potential clients where they'd heard about our services. The guy never popped up looking for retribution, but it became a practice I continued to practice the whole time I was in business. I needed to know people were really interested in hiring us, not trying to harm us. The incident also prompted me to hire more security for the girls. At that point, my brother was the only one doing security for us and we hired my god-brother also. He was 6'4" and nearly three hundred pounds. It helped that he was also a police officer, so I hired a few more off duty police officers he'd known to help out. They had no problem moonlighting with us, and it put everyone at ease, especially me. I was now focused strictly on booking parties that exclusive girls would attend. That meant, the girls listed under Kandi's were the only ones contracted at the event. Clients had to pay half up front for our services to book the date and the balance when we showed up at the event. I didn't play that sharing money shit with other agencies trying to send their girls to the same event. That right there was the main reason I wanted to leave the strip club lifestyle to begin with. There were too many bitches fighting over four quarters from one broke ass nigga. If I wasn't willing to go through that, I for damn sure wasn't

willing to put any of my girls through it. Therefore, our contracts

backed and protected our every move and made sure we'd be the only

ones making money in the room.

In addition to that particular stipulation in our contracts, clients

had to pay a non-refundable deposit for our services. That way, we

were guaranteed to be paid. The deposit was equal to half the price of

the entire party, priced per girl. They paid one hundred fifty dollars per

dancer, half up front and the rest when they arrived. I didn't have time

for petty clients who didn't have money to spend. All clients had to

book a minimum of six girls and no maximum. If more than ten girls

were required, I would offer a deal, breaking the price down to one

hundred dollars per dancer, per contractual agreement. The clients

were still required to tip, so the girls would make money. I would book

our girls during a three-hour time span with an hour and a half

guaranteed. Clients were told that from the time of our agreed-upon

arrival, they were guaranteed an hour and a half of entertainment. So,

as long as the girls were making money past that time mark, the

entertainment continued. If the guys weren't spending money after the hour and a half timeframe had expired, the dancers were free and able to leave with an extra fee being added, if money and livelihood were not met.

The bottom line . . . if the guys stopped tipping, and the girls stopped making money, it wasn't worth our time and the girls would leave.

As the Madam, I took home the contract money, and the girls took home all their tip money. No tip out. Because my business would be paid via contract, no money at all would be taken from the girls at the end of every event. So, whatever they made would strictly go to them, once their paid time period expired. Even if there were a few extra girls who wanted to come last minute, and I knew the party would be big enough to accommodate them, I'd let them go too. I didn't make any contractual money from them, but I just wanted to create opportunities for girls to get paid for their hard work. Adding the additional girls always worked out, and it helped having them at the event, in case some girls didn't feel motivated to do shit. There were times when all they wanted was to make their money early and then sit the hell down. Some even played sick at the last minute, but I covered myself every time. I knew who the slackers were, and I was sure to enforce every single detail in my contracts.

From the way things operated, Kandi's was a revolutionary business at the time. Women just weren't running businesses like mine; businesses that promised their girls exclusivity so they didn't have to compete for attention and money with girls from other agencies. All my girls were guaranteed to make money and that's what we were all in it for. And lucky for me, that business model made Kandi's Dazzling Entertainment the place every pretty ass dancing girl in the city wanted to be.

After changing the name and doing business quite different than before, I'd had so many girls running through the company. The phone rang off the hook, and so many clients were requesting our services that I had no choice but to keep professional security on the payroll. That's just how big shit took off, and I mean that in the humblest way possible. The first four months of business, Kandi's Dazzling Entertainment was booked up every single weekend. It had gotten to a point where I ended up having to add weekdays to the schedule just to accommodate more clients. It wasn't long before the entire week was booked. I had nearly fifty girls on the payroll, and as more parties kept rolling in, I added fifty more. That was one hundred girls to keep track of, one hundred girls I had to look out for, and knowing the strengths and weaknesses of each of them, so I could match them with the right clients and send them to the right parties. It was hella work, and Dallas was still there to help me along the way.

"I told you this shit would pop off, didn't I?" she said as we were chit-chatting in the office. I was about to respond, but the phone rang before I could open my mouth.

"Kandi's Dazzling Entertainment. How may I assist you?"

"Hey Kandi," one of my client's asked. "I need your services for my event in two weeks. Baby, please tell me you're not booked, and please pencil me in."

The dude was one of my clients who had spent big dollars with us. I would always find a way to pencil him in, because he would make up any kind of party just to have my girls come through and entertain him. Without naming names, many people wouldn't believe the names on my client list.

"You know I have to ask how many girls, how many hours, what type of event and will it be at the same location?"

This particular client always cooked up something new, exciting and different. It was never the same ole shit with him, and girls liked to go to his parties because they knew the money would be right.

Once his party was scheduled, I looked at Dallas and laughed. Yet again, we couldn't even talk because the phone started ringing again. She held her hand on the receiver to stop me from picking up the phone.

"It's time for you to twerk off two phones. We're losing business if niggas can't get through and one phone ain't gonna work."

I had been thinking the same thing, so the next day, another line was finally added. It was typical that when someone called to book a party, I would go and see the location and meet with the guy to make sure the place was up to our standards and the girls would be safe. Being safe meant we arrived together and left together. I didn't give out addresses to the girls at all. I'd hire a driver so everyone could roll out together. There was safety in numbers and we wanted to make sure we got the party jumping when we arrived.

Word of mouth about my business kept spreading fast, and even The Motor City Casino had my business card blown up and on display. We must've done every single bachelor party for security guards working there at the time. To this day, I'm still 86'd from that casino; I was banned for solicitation. The casino stayed open for twenty-four hours, so after a night of dancing and turning up, me and my girls would hit the casinos. High rollers were all around us, so it was the best place to promote business and pick up new clients. Management saw my face there so much that they put my face and business card on display. It had gotten so bad that security wouldn't allow me to enter. I was escorted to the back office, where I was treated like a for real criminal by a chubby white man with a too tight suit on. I blew him off while sitting in a chair in front of his desk, chewing gum.

"For the last time, Kandi, you can't be soliciting at our casino!"

DETROIT MADAM

The direction of his eyes traveled up my smooth legs that looked like they'd been dipped in baby oil. He was trying to be serious, but lust filled his eyes.

"It might be soliciting to you, but it's business to me," I said. "Whether you admit it or not, the majority of those men out there are definitely interested in the services me and my girls are providing."

"Well, you can't provide it here. You're not welcomed here, and once you walk out that door, I never want to see your face again."

To this day, if my ID got swiped at the casino, I'll get what I like to call the two-finger tap. Security always shows up to escort my ass out. They didn't stop my show though. I had figured out so many other ways to reach some of the same people who frequented the casino. Many of them became regular clients, but to be honest, there were times when hassles occurred. Some guys refused to sign the contract, but so many of them did because we were the only real play in town. If they didn't use my services, they were shit out of luck. I was in a good position where I started to draw a line with contracts. It started when a dude named James had stopped by. I held a pen in one hand, the contract was in the other. James was one of my new difficult clients who I wasn't going to give a pass this time.

"Look, James. If you don't sign the contract, none of my girls will show up. I've been a little lenient in the past, but due to certain issues, everybody has to sign a contract."

He sighed, looked the contract over, and finally signed it.

"Here." He gave the contract back to me and grinned. "Y'all betta not be late, and make sure you come with them too."

As long as he paid the money and signed on the bottom line, I was good. I walked him to the door and told him that we would be there early. The night of the party, we arrived early and stayed late. James and his friends had a good time, and he never had a problem signing any future contracts I put in front of him. These situations taught me to always stand my ground and to never bend the rules for anyone.

Being in this business had its share of backstabbing bitches, too. If I found out that one of my girls went behind my back and did a party without my knowledge, I didn't fuck with her anymore. They were completely cut off from the money we were making, and were exempt from joining us at parties. This type of betrayal happened a lot. Simply because, some bitches eyes got bigger than they could control. Some of them started thinking they could master my job as Miss Madam, and run my business like I did. That was a big mistake, and once you fucked me over, I never let that shit happen again.

"Bu—but I thought one party on the side wouldn't hurt a damn thing." Val was trying to justify why she'd gone behind my back, when she'd signed a contract that prohibited it.

I came from behind my desk and stood face to face with her. She knew she had fucked up, and didn't dare look me in the eyes.

"I had yo back and you should've had mine too," I said. "One party does hurt, and what you did let me know that I can't trust you. You will never get another chance to do a party under my name again."

I escorted that bitch right to the door. I even wished her well, even though I knew she'd never make the kind of money she'd made with me again.

Val was only one of the many bitches who breached their contract and thought they could do the job better than me. It turned out that one chick who was working with me was an under-aged runaway. I didn't know that at that time. She wouldn't really dance that much at parties, and I wasn't the kind of boss that forced people to do anything. If she didn't want to make money, then that was on her. There was always going to be another girl waiting to take her place— waiting to make her money. My job was to make sure that hot girls showed up. That's it. So, not only was she under-aged, but her thing was really selling drugs, not dancing. I let her work one more good party for me, before I confronted her ass as we were leaving.

"That party was dope," she said, fake laughing and hanging all over me, as we made our way to the car. I pulled away from her and halted my steps. Seriousness was trapped in my eyes; she knew I wasn't playing.

"It's always dope, but you've been let go. Not only did you lie to me about yo age, but I made it clear that I don't fuck around with girls who do or sell drugs. I've been watching you, and yo ass gotta go."

Her mouth dropped wide open; she was stunned by what I'd said. "I never lied to you about my age and I told you I was twenty-one. As for the drugs, what drugs are you talking about? I don't do or sell drugs."

She denied all of it, but like always, I had connections and evidence to back shit up. A copy of her ID was in my purse. When I showed it to her, her face fell flat. I also gave her the name of the nigga inside she'd tried to sell drugs to.

"Bye bitch," I said, waving as I walked off. "I wish you well."

She stood there looking stupid as fuck. Eventually, she tried to branch off and do her own thing while selling drugs on a bigger scale with the cartels. She also tried to compete with me, but to no avail. Niggas ended up robbing her and her girls. That's how she ended up strictly selling drugs. That didn't work out either, and she later ended up doing fed time behind her drug business. I never saw her again.

On the flipside, I did have a few girls who I considered my equal. Our relationships became friendships. One of them had a carwash, and if my girls didn't have anything to do, I'd take them to her carwash to work and get things popping. In those cases, however, my friend and I had an understanding. She didn't try to steal my girls, and I didn't try to steal her girls. We kept our camps, for the most part, very separate. I'd tell my girls, "If you wanna go over there with them, take yo ass over there, but ain't no coming back. Things would get too messy, and there was no way for any of them to try to be in two cliques at once.

Some girls thought the rules were too much, but without them, success wouldn't have come as quickly as it did. I'd learned from my partnership with Monte that specific rules, and sticking to them, made a business work. I didn't miss doing business with him at all, and at twenty-four years old now, I was learning on all fronts. Every single thing down to the smallest detail of my company was legit. I was scared to go to jail, and I'd seen so many people around me getting locked up. There was no way that I could control *everything* that happened at these parties, though. So many parties had been raided around town, but none of them were parties we were at.

Some girls were being charged with prostitution. So even though my business was more on a private, exclusive level, I still had thoughts of going to jail on my mind. Whenever girls and guys mixed with drinking and drugs, anything could pop off. My girls weren't supposed to do no drugs. I lectured them about it, and it was important for them to always keep a clear head. Unfortunately, some of them didn't listen. That's what scared me the most, so behind the scenes, I worked extremely hard to protect my business reputation and made sure everything on my end stayed legit. It did, but again, sometimes shit still popped off. That's just how it was in this business, and it was easy to stumble upon trouble.

For instance, that day, a man at a party tipped one of my girls to dance. For whatever reason, she wasn't in the mood so she wasn't dancing to his liking. He felt like she wasn't doing her job entertaining him and getting him off. When they waved me over to settle the dispute, I told the DJ to cut the music and settled it like this, while standing between them.

"Look, we don't give no money back," I said to him, and then faced the girl. "Honey, you better flip and dip and do whatever the hell you need to do. Give him a few more dances, but" I turned to the man, again, "like it or not, we ain't giving no money back. That ain't how it goes."

He yelled and started making a scene. "Aw, hell nah! Y'all bitches ain't going nowhere til I get my money back!"

Yet again, he was another nigga tripping with a gun. He pulled it out and started waving it around. My girl dipped behind me, while I just stood there looking at his ass like he was crazy. Now, we weren't in Detroit, where I was well known in the streets for parties like this. We were out in Inkster, in BMF territory. Many people were familiar with the song "Blowin' Money Fast," but in Inkster, BMF was a real person who was in jail now. So Inkster had some grimy ass niggas. They noticed the commotion and started to gather around, since ole boy had his gun out.

"What the fuck is up!" Another nigga shouted and whipped out his pistol too. "These bitches ain't tryin' to get ova on you, are they?"

"Hell yeah they are. Bitch don't wanna dance, so I want my fuckin' money back." My security not liking how the situation was going pulled out their guns.

A few other niggas got trigger happy too, and as they surrounded us with guns drawn, I'm not gon' lie, I started feeling real fucked up inside. I kept my brave face on, but was dying inside while staring at so many guns. Luckily for me, a higher upper dude I knew in

Inkster stepped in and put an end to the shit. He was mad by how we'd been treated, and he cursed all them niggas out.

"Are you muthafuckas crazy!" he yelled while looking around at those fools. "Put them fuckin' guns down and don't be treatin' my girl Kandi like that! You niggas about to start a war. Don't y'all ever disrespect her, and I'll kill all you muthafuckas if you ever do this shit again!"

With stupid looks on their faces, one by one, they lowered their guns. He even made them apologize, before walking me and my girls out of that situation. I'd realized how much respect I'd earned, even outside of Detroit. In addition to that, my girls respected me more and more—I rode hard for mine. Niggas knew we weren't giving no refunds, and if you paid for a dance, that's what you got, whether you liked it or not. Preferences didn't have shit to do with me, period. And if they didn't like how my girls *moved*, they were always encouraged to take their business elsewhere.

Chapter Thirteen

An important attribute to being the Detroit Madam was I took care of my girls, as well as my clients. For the most part, I had developed great relationships with everyone and that tremendously worked to my benefit. One of our first major parties on Prairie Street was for a guy by the name of Roger. He and all his friends were Detroit police officers who had booked me for their bachelor parties— it was some shit I'll never forget to this day. Roger was a short, smart, and very cool dude. He reminded me of Joe Pesci from *Goodfellas*, and always had me cracking up. Known as the good boy I turned bad, he had been in law enforcement for a long time. He came from a well-to-do family of politicians, with a few underworld players in the family gene pool as well. I often referred to him as my connect because he was well connected, and 80 percent of our parties came from him. His political and some form of law background were beneficial to me in every way. But with me, he went from being a traditional, good ole boy to being completely turned out. He had girls lined up to swing and dance for him. I'd met him at a party that day, and it was the start of a solid business relationship with us. He was finally settling down to marry the woman he'd been with for years, but the nigga still had a mistress.

While at his bachelor party, he was so geeked, which only heightened the Napoleonic complex his little ass already had. Everything he did, he wanted to do it in an over-the-top way. He wanted to stand out, to be loud, to have his voice heard and be noticed. I was there to help him do it. We partied hard and everyone was so hyped. But when Roger's mistress attempted to step in and hang all over him, he wasn't having it.

"Why don't you go over there and sit for a while," he said, removing her hand off his shoulder. "I'm not even sure why you're here, and now isn't the time to be hanging all over me."

Her feelings looked hurt as she blinked away her tears and trotted away. She took a seat in the far corner, watching as Roger and his friends had more than a good time. He had booked fifteen to twenty girls, and he and his buddies were busy getting turnt. There was stuff going on *everywhere*. There were girls on the dance floor, girls on the balcony, and plenty of girls in the basement. Girl-on-girl shows were in action and money was flying all over the place. Meanwhile, I could see steam coming from his mistress' ears. She was big mad, but tried to pretend that she wasn't. She couldn't contain herself in the chair, so she got up and kept following Roger around. He was annoyed by her presence, and became less bothered with her and more focused on my girls.

"Yeah, baby," he said with his hands in the air, as one of the girls was bent over in front of him, shaking her ass. There was no breathing room in between them, and with his dick pressed against her butt, they might as well had been fucking. "Shake that ass, girl! Daaaamn, I like this shit!"

His mistress witnessed firsthand how his dick swelled in his pants and grew longer as my girl kept grinding on him. She had blown his mind, and he was like a kid in the candy store grabbing shit. His mistress had seen enough. She stormed out of the room, but he was so busy that he didn't even know she'd left. He must've realized that he'd brought sand to the damn beach when he brought his mistress to his bachelor party. That was a big mistake, and I'd told him, just like I had told many other men before . . . if yo girl can't handle it, leave her ass at home.

Many women couldn't handle seeing their men let loose, especially during our girl-on-girl shows that were a hit. We passed a hat around the room and told the guys, "If you wanna see more girl-on-girl shows, everybody in here has to put ten dollars in this hat."

The hat got passed around, and within a few minutes, it overflowed with ten dollar bills. It was so successful that we started doing that shit at all of the parties. Depending on the size of the party there would be thousands of dollars in a hat for the girls to split. All that money just for doing one show, for five minutes. Roger was excited by the girl-on-girls shows. They turned him on for real, and by the end of the party, he was down a mistress, but had gained a friend for life.

"Oh, my God, Kandi!" he shouted in awe while hugging me. "I'm about to tell all my friends about your parties!"

When I say he'd told *all* his friends, he literally did! He was one of my best clients, and if the schedule was already booked, it went to being *over*booked. He had so many connections it was crazy. Police officers and politicians were some of my biggest clients, and from the

Detroit police force, to the Southfield police force, to the Oak Park police force, we had them on lock.

Roger had gotten so bold with the shit that he started bringing his fiancée, who later became his wife, to the parties. Surprisingly, she was just as geeked as he was about the parties, and every time he talked to me about them, he kept reminiscing about what had happened.

"I'll never forget that party you all did for my stepbrother in Indiana, when you brought at least twenty-five girls," he said, laughing over the phone. "A bitch gave my brother head that night while he was getting a dance from another bitch! And if you remember, my homeboy Donny Thumb got his name from sticking his thumb up a girl's ass that same night. It was off the hook!"

To my recollection, I didn't see any of that, but I wasn't oblivious to what could've been going on. However, per my business guidelines, I offered strictly professional entertainment. None of what he'd said to me was really my business, but I laughed right along with him, while penciling in his next party on the schedule.

DETROIT MADAM

Building relationships like the one I'd had with Roger was vital. And many men around Detroit especially, knew me as the Madame of the town who supplied all the hottest girls in the city, even though, technically, Kandi's was all about party entertainment and not sexual entertainment. Some of the things I'd heard was taking place at parties were mind-blowing, but not unbelievable because that's just how wild shit used to be back then. Bitches did what they chose to do to get money, and used to fuck and suck and fuck and suck at their own leisure. And I did what I did best, which was count the money I'd made from bookings and mind my own damn business. Still, day after day, and night after night, everybody was eager to spill the beans and share what was really happening on the inside of *some* of these parties.

"Girrrrrl," Tammy said as we walked down the street. She was on her way to pick up her son, and stopped to chat when she saw me. "I have never made so much money in my life! One hour of my time was worth it, and after I made what I needed, I was outta there. Money was being thrown all over the place. Besides that, I had fun. Shit been stressing me out lately, but I had fun that night. Thanks for hooking me up, though. And don't forget to holla at me when the next party comes."

"You know I will. I'll never forget in my life how much fun we had at that first party. We were so lit that you instantly became a part of the crew."

"Well, thanks again for letting me in so I could run wild," she laughed and gave me a hug. "I gotta go get my son, but I'll check in with you later."

Tammy walked off and I got into my car thinking about what she'd said. It felt good to help girls make as much money as they needed, and it damn sure beat giving some of these broke ass niggas something for nothing. Of course, I didn't publicly condone things that were going on at these parties, because per the contract, that's not what they were hired to do. But I liked the fact that my girls were in control, and whenever they would reach their personal goal for the night, many would chill out for the rest of their time at the event or go hide somewhere so they wouldn't be bothered. Each girl would have their own personal quotas. One might just want to make rent. Another might want to walk out with several Gs so she grinded all night long. As long as everyone left together, I was good. Safety, again, was important, and a lot of times there were additional parties we had to attend, right after the previous one. Sometimes, I'd have to go looking for my girls. One would be in this room, another would be somewhere else. No matter where they were, I was always sure to tell them to pick up every last dollar, before we left. Tons of money would be all over the fucking place, so it wasn't hard to believe that some of them were capping out within an hour and wanted to go somewhere and chill. The only times nobody really wanted to chill was at the parties Roger had booked. Every girl wanted to attend those parties, because they knew they'd leave with hella money. We could never stop talking about how much we'd made from his parties, and Roger couldn't stop calling to tell me how much the parties had changed his life for the better.

"Man what?" he said, laughing, again, as I'd bragged about my crew. "A part of the crew? Your crew turned us the fuck out! You didn't forget about telling me how to go about getting a threesome from my girl, did you?"

"Nah, I didn't forget," I said. "I told yo ass while you are fucking her good, that was the perfect time to ask for one. Did you do it?"

"Damn right I did. I wanted to wait until I told you what happened. I was fucking her so good that she told me she'll do whatever I want. Before I knew it, we were going crazy with bitches. Kandi, yo crazy ass the reason we became swingers. You showed me the way and turned me out!"

I didn't mind passing on tips to help people improve their sex lives, and in addition to Roger, many of my clients would always seek advice from me. Unfortunately, I never charged for that advice. But every person . . . every couple had to do what worked for them. It was nobody's business but their own.

"I told you it would work, didn't I? You can ask her anything during sex, while you hitting it. A woman gon' say yes to whatever, especially if you hitting it right."

My ongoing advice changed everything, and his girl was just as thrilled as he was about the encounter. Tammy took credit for allowing them to free themselves. She always reminded me that if it wasn't for her *skills*, things might have turned out differently for Roger.

"I was seasoned," Tammy said. "Roger and his woman weren't, and it was more of a let's just hook up type of thing when the both of them asked me to join them. It wasn't the best experience for me, because it was their first time. But yeah, I was Roger's first threesome."

Even after his marriage fell apart, Roger was still Roger—the Roger we'd helped him be. He'd always say, "I want a girl who wants to please *me*."

So many men had the same mindset, and I once heard him call a woman and say, "Baby, I'm gonna come pick you up later, and we're gonna do a show in front of this girl. Are you with it?"

The woman was like, "Yeah, whatever you want, Daddy."

He'd be specific like, "I want her to be soaking wet in the back seat looking at us. You hear me?"

"Yes, baby! What time you coming to pick me up?"

I couldn't believe how aggressive his approach had gotten; he had completely changed. Then again, he hadn't. It had all been buried inside of him, and like so many other men I'd met, they were just waiting for a moment to free themselves. My girls and I were just there to help in any way we could. We woke up every day, ready to do this shit over and over again.

Chapter Fourteen

The women of Kandi's Dazzling Entertainment made a mark in Detroit, and word of mouth about who they were traveled faster than water flowing down a river. Girls from Atlanta, Chicago, Tennessee . . . to name a few places, came to Detroit just to dance and be down with the gang. To say that I was proud would be an understatement because that's just how banging my business was at the time. Don't get me wrong, I appreciated every single girl who came around and helped make the business what it was, but my core girls . . . them muthafuckas were my bitches! It wasn't no secret who they were.

Girls were always in and out of Kandi's Dazzling Entertainment, but these bitches were down with me until the very end. I have nothing but love for them, and I meant those words from the bottom of my heart. The core group was like family. We ate together, rode together, slept together, partied together—Dallas and I even lived together—had fun together and got into bullshit together. After the parties, we'd all come back to my house, sometimes, to drink, shoot the shit, and talk about what had gone down that night. And then we'd pass out—some girls strewn over the couches, others all over the floor. We'd be still in our dance outfits, sprawled out everywhere asleep. Most of the time, we wouldn't wake up until around noon or one in the afternoon. I mean, bitches had responsibilities, but then again, some of them didn't. I surely did, and had hired a nanny to help me with my kids. She was the best nanny ever, and my kids loved her. That was important to me, especially since me and my girls were out so much living the party life. Some of them still lived at home with their parents, and since no one wanted to walk into their mama's house at four o'clock in the morning, they just stayed with me for the night. On most days, I'd go get something to eat, we'd hit the mall by two or three, hit the strip by about five, and then get ready for another party around eight. That was the routine and the way our lives were structured.

So, DetroitStallion, E-Boogy, Dallas, of course, Diamond and Tammy were my main, everyday bitches who were the faces of Kandi's Dazzling Entertainment. When you thought of the business you thought of us hands down, because nine times out of ten, us six would be the main girls showing up to the majority of events with a mindset of going hard or going home. And, trust me, we went so fucking hard that it still amazes me to this very day.

The DetroitStallion and I went way back to my earlier dancing days when I first hit the stage. She was my bitch for real. Standing about 5'10", brown skinned and bowlegged, we often times looked at her as our personal Ronny from Players Club, because once we were out at an event or putting on a show, she demanded attention and respect, no matter what. If it wasn't given, she'd knuckle up and that was a fact. People throughout the city were scared as fuck of her, because like I'd said, with her, respect was given at all times. That's just how it was, and niggas loved her because of her bold moves, whenever it was her time to shine. She was freaky as hell, and her famous act was pulling glassy marbles out of her vagina. They weren't small marbles either. These were big . . . like tension marbles you put in your hands and rolled around as a stress reliever. That's the type of skills she had and everyone loved it. The crowd would go crazy, and niggas acted like they lost their mind when they saw her in action.

"Daaaaaaamn," voices echoed throughout the thick crowd. There was nowhere to stand and watch, but people stood on chairs and tables just to get a glimpse of the DetroitStallion. She was so damn skilled and emptied wallets wherever she went.

"Baby, you can have all my money," a dude said, tossing every last dollar in his pocket at her. "Do that shit again!"

Without hesitation, she did it again and again. Most people were confused and thought it was easy because how effortlessly she performed. Little did they know, it took a lot of skill and pussy muscle to hold the marbles in and push them out one at a time. But, she'd mastered how to do it and her shows were on fire. She was so cold with the shit that in the middle of her shows, she would lay on her back, twerk her legs wide open and release them bitches out of her pussy like it was a piece of cake.

Another dancer who had opened doors for Kandi's Dazzling Entertainment was the original E-Boogy who was known as the number one stunna out of the group because she wasn't with all the extra shit. She was, however, the cutest of them all—most people would say. She didn't really have many standout factors about herself, with the exception of being a yella girl. Light-skinned girls didn't have to do a lot, and in this business, being light-skinned alone was enough.

DETROIT MADAM

Us dark-skinned girls had to do extra shit to get that same attention as E-Boogy. But her light skin caught niggas' attention fast. She had them rolling in from left to right, every time I turned my damn head. Her banging ass body was an asset, too, and it was easy for niggas to fall head over heels for her. She didn't do any special shows, no flips no nothing. All she did was show the fuck up, while they did multiple shows a night, handstands, flips, tricks, acrobatics and popped coochies all night. She'd walk around with a seductive grin on her face, while flirting her ass off.

"I'm not dancing tonight," she'd say all the time to niggas who pulled her in their direction. "But I'll be more than happy to sit on yo lap and share a few drinks wit' you."

She'd sit, but wouldn't drink shit. Many niggas thought if they got her drunk, she'd do something extra. She never did and still got paid for her time. They didn't even want her to dance; chilling with them seemed satisfying enough.

Neither of us was short on money, ever, because business was going well. We'd mastered how to get exactly what we needed, and E-Boogy's pockets stayed fatter than most. Whenever we'd go out, she would be the first one to pull out cash and say, "I got it. One of my boys gave me a few dollars, so order or buy whatever 'cause bitches we guuuud!"

It was her favorite thing to call niggas she messed with: the boys. We just rolled with it because 'the boys,' as she called them, really took good care of her because of her looks. Outside of that, E-Boogy was down for the gang and she had our backs. That's what we all appreciated about her, and on any given day, we could always count on her to show up and be down to ride, even if she didn't want to.

"E, bitch," I would say on the phone. "What you got up for the night? You doing this party or what?"

"I hadn't planned to 'cause I'm tired as hell. But fuck it. If you need me, I'm there. What time I need to be ready?"

That's why we fucked with E-Boogy as hard as we did. She was rarely ever late, and her word to show up was bond.

Then there was Diamond. I wouldn't necessarily say she was our thug-life girl because DetroitStallion had that status on lock. But Diamond was most certainly the life of the party and you'd better fucking believe it. Although Diamond wasn't the best-looking girl out of the group, we often compared her to rapper Foxy Brown because she was very skinny, about 5'2" and had brown skin just like the rapper herself. She also had hella swag, and niggas liked that she was a little rough around the edges. She wasn't only a part of Kandi's Dazzling Entertainment; she was also a part of the Outcasts, a motorcycle club that was one of the most infamous clubs known throughout the city. The Outcasts were known for drugs and doing many other illegal activities. They legit had it going on, and were on some type of real-life, hardcore motorcycle venture you'd see at the movies or on TV. The founder's name was Samuel Day. He had a reputation for turning young girls out on cocaine, but was handsome as hell. His trick was to meet a young girl and coax her into believing she was in a relationship with him. Then he'd end up turning her out. After that, the motorcycle club would prostitute the girls out. Diamond was one of the girls he'd turned out.

By the time I'd met her she'd escaped that lifestyle and was no longer under Samuel's thumb. She was married to a Lion's NFL player, but they were separated. Diamond had become accustomed to the cocaine lifestyle. Even as she was married to the Lion's player, her habit only had room to grow bigger and bigger—only, I didn't know that. I didn't know she and her hubby were known for spending racks and racks on coke. When we'd met, her husband was trying to get her back, but she was on the run from him, dancing with my girls and living her life to the fullest away from him. This bitch would party and dance all night long, if I needed her to. She was the number one girl I would always call on for bookings, because on the inside of several hot magazines in Detroit, her face would be next to words like: *the life of the party*! She could be having the worst day of everyone in America, but no matter what she was dealing with, it still didn't stop her from having the time of her life at parties we booked.

Each and every girl in the core group had something different and original they'd brought to the gang. But that bitch Tammy, she was really down with the shits. Roger was forever grateful to her for joining in on his first threesome, and she was a big part of why he kept coming back to book parties. So, to be quite honest, she was the crazy muthafucka who *really* turned this nigga out. She wasn't shy when it came to nobody, and many of the connects she'd made, she flipped their worlds upside down.

Any and everything you can think of, we did it together. We'd all squeeze into my bathroom to get ready. There would be two or three girls in the tub trying to wash up in the shower, while three more of us squeezed in front of the mirror applying eyeliner, mascara and putting on thongs. We didn't wear a lot of makeup, but we made sure E-Boogy did our hair. MAC didn't exist back then; we had some 526 Wet n' Wild makeup that suited us just fine. We didn't even have lashes—just hair, foundation, eyeliner and lip color. So, if you were ugly, baby, you learned how to deal with that ugliness! There were, what some people might say, *ugly* girls on the team, but those girls were ones who went to parties and set shit off. They were the wildest and made everyone else feel wild too. Every single person on our squad had a purpose. We all had something we were good at or a skill we were known for. That was never clearer than at one party we did. I went in thinking it was going to be a normal night, and even though the man who'd booked the party had already paid the contractual down payment, his buddy he was throwing the party for refused to play ball.

He held the second half of my money hostage, until I was willing to line the girls up against the wall, like some chorus girls, for a fucking inspection.

"Line 'em all up and tell them to pull up their shirts," he demanded like he was some type of sergeant in the army. "Stomachs exposed. I need to do a stomach check. I don't want no railroads. If a girl looked like a railroad track ran across her stomach, she can't dance here!"

The muthafucka was so serious! I had never experienced anything like it, even though I had seen my share of disrespectful niggas. All of our mouths were dropped wide open. Since he was paying *his* money, I let him choose who he wanted to dance that night and who he didn't. He really did sit a couple of my girls down, but in the end, I told them I'd put in the extra work so we'd all get paid. I didn't want them to come there and waste their time. It was only fair that they got paid, too.

Later in the night, things shifted. Dude was drunk off his ass, as were all the men. They didn't know who the hell was doing what, and threw money everywhere. The girls who'd been benched slipped right in and made all the money they could. They led with conversation, poured more drinks for the men, and even danced for them, no matter what their stomachs looked like. It worked out for everyone, but that night was some true Don type shit. It was the only night I'd ever seen the birthday boy go home with more money than my girls did. People brought him nice gifts, even exclusive alcohol bottles . . . not like bottles in the liquor store, but some huge ass bottles of alcohol I'd never even seen before. He even got shoeboxes full of money, and he wasn't no frivolous nigga either. He boxed up his shit and took his money with him! He was the only one not making *shit* rain.

That was one night when we learned that "ugly" to some men, could mean a whole new thing. But we rode with it and made our money any damn way. We also were sure to keep E-Boogy around to help us look our best.

Getting back to the squad, what fucked up people the most about Tammy was the fact that she was so quiet, laid back . . . reserved, whereas everyone else in our group was loud and aggressive as hell. She stood out because, not only was she quiet, she had body for days. I'm talking big titties and a big ole juicy ass. She was high yellow as well, and once niggas seen her in the act, they couldn't believe it because she was so quiet.

Every time I talked to her, and we would travel down memory lane, her description of what we did was summed up like this, "We were bold with our shit, and involved ourselves with people that were in notorious gangs without even knowing it at the time. That's just how fast it was with us. The money was just like selling drugs. It came in fast and it went quick. We went shopping, played drinking games, did Super Bowl parties, events at huge ass halls, barbershops, road trips, you name it. I mean, we did it all and there was hella money to make back then. The strip club wasn't making no money, so it was us. We made it happen for sure. Nobody will ever be able to follow in our footsteps and do what we did."

I wholeheartedly agreed with her assessment. It was a hard act to follow, but so many bitches tried to walk in our steps. Tammy was the one who observed everything from the smallest to the biggest. She would see how intimidated we would make bitches when we stepped in events and clubs. She elaborated on those times as well.

"When we walked in, no other bitches existed, and don't forget most of these events were private anyways. At times, we rolled in from fifty to one hundred bitches deep, and that's where the intimidation came in. But that didn't matter because there was so much money on the table for everybody."

I nodded and started traveling down memory lane with her that day. We could talk for hours about the past. It never got old to us.

"Aye Tammy, remember our theme song was Fifty Bitches Deep by Drunken Master and Lola Damone?" I laughed and shook my head. "We piled in those cars like sardines, didn't we?"

"Girl, yes, and that's really what it was. We had so many bitches from all different walks of life dancing with us. I don't even think you knew what my occupation was during the day back then, did you?"

"Now that I think about it, hell naw!" I paused and waited for her to say something top tier. "What did you do, girl?"

"Girl, I was a schoolteacher by day, and you know, a fucking whatever at night. I wouldn't call myself an escort or anything like that. I was just a fun girl at night that was always down with showing niggas a good time."

She nailed it. Down for her clique, quiet and about her money—which described Tammy to the tee. Like many of us had known, she also knew dating at the time was out of the question because of the lifestyle she lived. It was hard to find a man in your corner and keep him. Many viewed dancers as hoes and didn't want to wife'em. But they didn't realize that's how we looked at them niggas too. They were the ones being tricked out of their money, and once a trick, always a trick. I didn't take any of them seriously.

"From the ages of eighteen or nineteen to twenty-six or so," she said. "We lived a wild ass life. Dating was out of the question, and things were much different than they are now."

"Way different. We didn't have social media. Imagine if we did! Our asses would've shown up all over the place. Whatever happened at those parties, stayed at those parties."

"Yep. And we pressed the issue of no cameras. Remember?"

I snapped my fingers and laughed. "Ooooh, I forgot about that. I used to make guys put their cameras up. If they had a camera, they got put out. That was a part of our discreteness, but because none of

our families knew, that's how it had to be."

Tammy and I spoke for hours that day. And while none of us

chose to date, Dallas did. Sis had sponsors out the woodworks coming

to take care of her from left to right. All the girl really had to do was

wink an eye or show a little teeth, and niggas would be willing to take

care of her for the rest of her life. That light-skinned shit with a nice

ass worked every single time. I wasn't mad about it one bit, because I

always believed that if you got it, use it to your fucking advantage. She

even dated a guy who was clueless about what we did, but when he

found out, they agreed that she would never come in the house with

less than five hundred dollars each night. If she was going to continue

in this profession, he wanted to make sure she brought home some

good money. The two of them were together for a minute, but before

she'd met him, she had sponsors rolling in like crazy who hooked her

up.

Without even having to say it, Dallas' crazy ass was topnotch

to me. The role she played in the group was simply being my best

friend and doing every single thing she could to keep us on top. From

214

security, to the group manager, to the assistant, to the dancer . . . Dallas did it all from A to Z. She was down with whatever I wanted to do, and remains my best friend to this very day. She did what the fuck she wanted to do, and I didn't have a problem with it at all because she had legit privileges, as best friend always did.

One memorable moment I'll never forget was a time when we went to a party and Dallas got so fucked up that I had to have my brother, who was also head of security, come get her ass and take her home. This particular night, we were playing what we called 'The Drinking Game.' You can just about guess what we were doing with that! Dallas tossed back so many different drinks, and even though she'd kept trying to pass on some of the drinks, it didn't help because she was already too far gone. She'd left the room, and I was looking for her for about thirty minutes.

"Where the hell is she at?" I asked while moving through a group of people at the party. I kept asking if anyone had seen her, but everyone shook their heads, implying no. I wound up finding her upstairs in the bathroom, passed the hell out. Saliva dripped from her mouth, her clothes were disheveled, and she was snoring her ass off.

DETROIT MADAM

It's funny as hell now, but at the time, I was so upset with her because the main things to remember were don't get drunk, don't do drugs, and a trick was always going to be a trick. Nothing more, nothing less. And there this bitch was, slumped and passed out in the bathroom at a party in front of new booties. I yanked her arm and tried to drag her out of there.

"Dallas, get yo ass up. You up in here in front of the new booties drunk as hell and making us look bad. This shit don't make no sense. These broads supposed to be looking up to you, and if one of they asses had done this, they'd be fired!"

She mumbled back and tried to straighten her head to look at me. It was limp and looked too heavy to lift. "Girrrrl, oh, my God, I know. I—I just drank the wrong shiiiiit . . ."

My brother had to come inside and carry her out of there. During that time it was early in the business and we were all still living together. When they got home, he put her on the bathroom floor by the toilet, in case she woke up in the middle of the night and had to throw up. By the time I'd gotten home, which was hours later, she was still laying in the same spot. I couldn't help but look back and laugh now at our wild and crazy lifestyle. The seasoned girls knew she normally didn't get messed up like that; it was really out of character for her. We were only a few months into this third company then, and as my right hand, she was smart as hell, and was such a mama bear to both the girls and me. She had always been the most tenured of my girls, the one who'd been there since the very start. That meant she was also the one who always directed the rookies—the new booties, as we called them, straight from Players Club—and told them what to do. She was out there dancing side by side with them because I couldn't do it all the time. I was overseeing and collecting the money. Sometimes, if we were short a girl, because I'd spread us a little too thin, I'd put on an outfit, but I never really went out there and danced. Instead, Dallas took a new booty up under her wings to show them the ropes. That's what friends did for me, and Dallas was the best of them all.

Chapter Fifteen

By this time, Kandi's Dazzling Entertainment was well known throughout the city of Detroit for the crazy, yet top-of-the-line parties we threw around the city. Even with that reputation, I never really had any concrete goals for the business. We were just having fun. I considered it all just good fun. I never really wanted it to become a serious part of my life because my mama lived in the city, and to my mama I was a good girl—a mother's girl. The business could've gone a lot further, but I was scared of her finding out about it. At the same time, Heidi Fleiss had recently been under fire, and I didn't want to end up like she did. I feared what happened to her would happen to me. That wasn't what I wanted to be known for, even though it *was* what I was known for. I just couldn't see myself taking it to the next level, but there were so many opportunities to do so right in front of me.

In the beginning of 2002, Dallas left Detroit and moved to Alabama with her man because his family lived there. That was pretty much the end of her streak in the business. Not too long after that, at the end of 2002, we had the infamous Manoogian Mansion party, which was the fatal moment for our Detroit mayor. There was a titty party at his mansion and the wife was supposed to be headed out of town. For whatever reason, she turned around after she'd left the house and the mayor thought the coast was clear. When she arrived back at the mansion, one of my girls, Sunshine, was in the midst of giving the mayor a lap dance.

"What in the fuck is going on here?" the wife shouted while looking around at the numerous partygoers in her house. Before Sunshine could make a move, the wife snatched her up and started pounding all over her face and head with her fist. Sunshine didn't stand a chance, and according to her, not many people were willing to intervene.

Bottom line, the wife wasn't having that shit. She may have been a mayor's wife, but she was still about her street business. She beat the shit out of Sunshine that day. The mayor's wife claimed it was just a slap, but even the nurse on duty in the ER that night said it was more than "just a slap." A few months later, in April 2003, Strawberry ended up dead. To this very day, they say someone associated with the mayor killed her or had something to do with it. I didn't know if that was true or not because Sunshine had a lot of other shit going on as well. She used to be involved in setting niggas up to get robbed. I assumed she just got caught up, and her untimely death just happened to be not long after her altercation at the Manoogian Mansion party. Either way, the mystery is unsolved and her case is still ongoing.

As all of that was going on, my life was spinning crazily from party to party. The nanny was still helping with my kids, so they didn't see a lot. They reaped the financial benefits and didn't want for much. But, at the same time, I knew I was in deep. I knew the business had exploded into something I'd always hoped for, but never really dreamed of. Even something I wasn't prepared for.

The deeper I went in, the wilder the parties became. The more off the chain, the more outrageous. One party that set us aside from any strip club or after party was an infamous loft party we did around 2003. I'd like to consider this party a high class event of my time as the Detroit Madam because some of the most prominent men, who shall remain nameless, were there. Many of these men have since become senators, attorneys, councilmen, CEOs of million-dollar companies and so much more. They showed my business what it was like to party with the prestigious, elite and top-notch gentlemen's club of Detroit city. It was where I'd met Sincere; he was the one who had booked the party with me. I went to the Lofts in Downtown Detroit to inspect the location before finalizing the details. Immediately falling in love with the location, I froze when I saw a mixture of sophistication, but roughness at the same time. I always loved the thin line that separated the two, because that was where a lot of people lived in their lives.

Mr. Sincere, a lawyer in the making, greeted me with the warmest smile I'd ever seen. Seeing him in a tailored suit with Cole Haans on was like a breath of fresh air. He had that rugged underlying look, but sophisticated arrogance that many business men in Detroit have. He was tall, light-skinned, nicely cut in all the right places and was handsome as ever. I always had a personal shoe problem myself—it was definitely one of the first things I paid attention to whenever men were around me. I thought if the rest of his friends at the party looked like him, the girls were going to make hella money and definitely have some eye candy to go with it. Being around good looking men always made the parties that much more fun.

With that in the back of my mind, I brushed off how fine he was and switched back to business mode. My pussy was already wet and giving me signals that it needed some attention, but I walked into his office like the boss I was. I took a seat, and as he was speaking, my eyes kept zooming in on his luscious lips.

"The bachelor party is for my best friend," he said. "I've hired some other girls as well, but based on your reputation around the city, I would really like for you and your girls to show up too."

"Understood, but unfortunately, according to the contract I just gave you, we aren't under any obligations to collaborate on any events with any other businesses. I would love to make this happen for you, but due to that particular stipulation, at this time, I will have to decline the entire offer." I stood and tucked my leather clutch underneath my arm. "Sorry for any inconvenience this may have caused you, and I hope you're able to book exactly what you're looking for."

Soon after my speech that I'd made many times before, I pivoted and headed towards the door. Sincere cleared his throat and quickly spoke up.

"I know your policy on being the only entertainer, but I guarantee your girls will make money or I will double your booking fee."

I couldn't give in that easy, so I swung around and hit him with a smile. "I'll think about it and let you know what I decide within one or two days. Until then, have a wonderful day, sir."

I walked out with some heavy shit on my mind. Of course, I was going to do it. Once he mentioned doubling the booking fee, it was a done deal. I had to let him sweat a little bit. I also needed to put my pussy in check, because it was screaming for that muthafucka during the whole meeting. After two days had passed, I called to let him know I'd drawn up a new contract, and instead of the normal half down deposit, the full fee was required upfront. As expected, he agreed.

"I have no problem with that," he said. "And I must say that I like how you do business. That was a boss move and I'm highly impressed."

"You're not the only one, and I'll see you soon enough to let you know how my girls and I treat men that we're impressed with. Thanks for your business. It's been a pleasure working with you."

I was hyped as hell about this party, and when it arrived, my brother drove his van to scoop up all fifteen of my girls so we could be on time and strut into the venue together. The second we arrived, it blew our minds back because of the luxury surrounding us. Don't get me wrong, Detroit had some nice ass places but this one was so unexpected. It was something like a beauty and the beast type of ordeal. Lofts weren't in back then, at least not in my world, so for us to walk into this type of space was every bit of mind blowing. There was exposed brick and painted pipes with no traditional ceilings above us. The floors were covered with beautiful, glowing cherry and a floor-to-ceiling fireplace lit up the whole area. The décor was rustic, and it kind of put us in the mindset of a cabin up north or in Tennessee. It was hard to believe we were in the city part of downtown.

Sincere lived in a loft on the third floor of the building, so the unit the party was in was vacant on the first floor. The way they decorated the venue, no one would have thought the space had been empty. To top it off, the niggas at the party wasn't dressed like your typical nigga at parties that we usually entertained. These niggas didn't come in t-shirts, jeans and gym shoes. They arrived in suit-like attire, their ties were undone, and with their sleeves rolled up, they were ready to relax from a hard day at work. I viewed it as a ratchet-formal event. A true grown and sexy party; I loved every bit of it.

As I'd mentioned before, these guys hadn't even reached their full potential yet. They were mostly in college, working towards some type of law degree or was affiliated with a popular fraternity. Every last one of them were sharp, but still had some hood in them. I could tell by the way they were conversing with some of the other girls who had already arrived. Since Sincere had paid upfront, along with other financial agreements, we paid the other chicks no mind and basically came in and took over.

The instant my girls walked in, they shut shit down. Music started thumping and money started rolling in. The girls that were there couldn't even fuck with my girls on any given day. They moved aside and watched the DetroitStallion work her marbles, E-Boogy shake her high yella ass, and one of my girls, Chocolate, performed her infamous milk show where she would squirt milk out of her breasts and the men would lick it off her body. Now, don't get me wrong, Chocolate was a grown ass woman who had kids a few years back. How she was able to hold that much milk in her breast years later, I didn't know. It still amazed me to this day, but she did it each and every time. Niggas loved it, especially on that particular night.

"Fucking wow," one nigga said as he stood with a group of men who had their eyes locked on my girls. "This shit is unbelievable!"

"You damn right it is," another one said. "It's about to be on tonight!"

They were chanting, high-fiving each other, dancing with my girls and having the time of their lives. DetroitStallion and those marbles sucked them in every time. Nobody blinked as she made huge marbles flow from her vagina, and our normal girl-on-girl show set it off. Niggas paid $500 each for two shows, on top of throwing a few racks in tips after they'd paid the show fee. There was so much going on, I couldn't even remember who the actual bachelor was. Each and every guy there had a grand time partying with the girls I'd brought to entertain. The party was such a vibe that when it was time for Sincere and I to go count up the rest of the funds from the event, we didn't even realize what was going on. We ended up in his loft on the third floor, laughing our asses off. He was sitting on a leather sectional looking hella good with his shirt unbuttoned, waves flowing, and facial hair trimmed just right. I was only a few feet away from him, holding a brick of money in my hand.

"Now that was a muthafucking party," he said. "It was nowhere near what I expected. You and your girls did the damn thing. Looks like Kandi's Dazzling Entertainment got it going on."

I was blushing my ass off. "Well, I told you we'd be worth it. I'm glad you listened and didn't walk away from my offer."

"I never walk away from an offer from a beautiful woman. And if you make me another one, I promise I'll bite on it."

He looked at my breasts that were clearly visible through the sheer fabric on my top. He was trying to start something, and you'd better believe I was about to finish it.

"I prefer that you make me an offer," I said. "Then, I'll determine if I accept it or not."

Sincere made his way to my side of the sectional and stood in front of me. As he removed his suit jacket, I reached out and started to remove his leather belt and unzip his pants. Before I could finish, he took my hand and pulled me up to him. What a fucking gentleman he was. There was no breathing room between us, and the feel of his body meshed with mine had me shook. I couldn't say shit, and was relieved when he covered my mouth with his, before slipping his tongue inside of it. While indulging in an intense kiss, I slipped my hand down his pants just to make sure his package was right. A bitch had to make sure *it* was worthy of my time. Normally, I was strictly business, and I didn't like mixing it with pleasure. But the size of that muthafucka made me rethink things. I had to try it out, and when I did, I rode that bitch until the wheels fell off. My mood matched his, and he was a nasty-talking nigga who fully energized me.

"Fuck the shit outta me, girl! Work that pussy and moisturize this dick wit' yo juices."

The thug side of him had shown up and I was there for all of it. He tampered with my cookie jar for nearly an hour, and afterwards, we left to go rejoin the party. Out of my whole career as a business owner, it was the first time anything like that had ever happened, especially while I was out on the job. He was just one of a kind, and I couldn't let an opportunity like that pass me by.

The two of us rejoined the party, as if nothing ever happened. Actually, it didn't according to everyone else because no one knew anything, outside of the two of us and Dallas. But the party had gotten out of control. The first thing I noticed was people outside on the patio being too loud. Some were naked while dancing to the music the DJ had bumped up too many notches. We had no idea how it had gotten that way, but shit had been turned up times ten. My bitches not only came with their own shows, but they came with toys too. All I saw was niggas getting their asses whooped by some of the girls who had whips in their hands. I couldn't believe that these men were some of the freakiest niggas we'd ever entertained.

"What's up with this?" I asked Sincere while looking around, stunned. "We weren't gone that long, were we?"

"I didn't even keep up with the time, but these niggas tripping. Tell yo girls to come back in here. I don't want my neighbors tripping or finding out what's really going on. Then we'll have to worry about the police. We don't need them muthafuckas showing up."

The majority of people were on the patio deck smoking blunts and getting lap dances, while drinks flowed like water. Gray smoke waffled throughout the air, and the smell of marijuana was potent. Shit was wild, but truthfully, fun as fuck. I did my best to calm things down, but it was so off the chain that when I opened the bathroom door, some random girl that wasn't a part of my group was passed out on the floor. Her girls had already left the party. I couldn't believe they'd done that shit, and I also couldn't believe that she'd put herself in a situation like this. If she was one of my girls, I would have fired her ass. Always looking out for the other woman, there was no way I could leave her alone and in that condition.

"Come on, sis, wake up," I said, patting her face with cold water. I kept moving her head, forcing her to wake up.

"Wha—where am I?" she stuttered. "I feel siiiick."

I pulled her over to the toilet, where she vomited, before falling back on the floor. It took a while for her to get herself together, but I doctored her back to good health. I hated to do it, but I lectured the fuck out of her grown ass, and pointed in her face while doing it.

"Whoever the hell you rode with left yo ass, which means you don't need to be riding with them no muthafucking more. You're responsible for you! You have to hold yourself accountable, and you should be paying attention to your surroundings. Don't ever do no shit like this again! Especially, not around all these rowdy niggas!"

Right after that, she joined my company and started rolling with my crew. Simply because, I proved to her that I gave a fuck about the people who rolled with me. That was the difference between a pimp and a madam. Pimps are users. He takes the women's money, beats them, degrades them, fucks with their minds, and a lot of times they get their women under false pretenses. But as a madam, I was all about taking care of my girls, making sure they made money and that they were physically and mentally okay. It was all about protecting them, and even though the party went on until four in the morning that day, I stuck by her side. Everyone was exhausted, and the few after parties we were supposed to attend had to wait for another day. Those parties weren't on the books, so we weren't obligated to go to them.

DETROIT MADAM

They were just extra setups we had on the side, if the girls wanted to stay out partying longer or pick up some extra cash at the next spot. But none of that was necessary with these niggas. They came with the shits, but none more than Sincere.

"What did I tell you?" Sincere yelled in my ear, so I could hear him over the loud music. "My niggas came correct, and I know all yo girls got paid big money tonight. Don't tell me they didn't!"

Yeah, his arrogance was a little annoying and that was a fact. But he was spot on with what he'd said. He kept trying to tell me he was going to throw another party, which I don't think he ever did. I was sure it was an attempt to get us to come turn his boys out once more. There were random times that Sincere would call me, but because I didn't want to mix business with pleasure again, I always made sure to never be available whenever he would try to reach out. Years later, we became great friends. I mentioned his name offhandedly one day as I was getting my hair done, and my stylist's ears perked up immediately.

"Wait, I know him! I grew up with him!" She called him up and we all joked and laughed. He was now a big-time lawyer in the state of Michigan, exactly what he'd been studying for when I'd met him. I would often go to him for legal advice, but because I wasn't into dating back then, I left that one-time loft situation exactly where it was.

No matter what backgrounds they came from, niggas from all around the city knew, if there was a party thrown, we were the girls to call. This fact was so well known that our presence was even requested all the way down in Myrtle Beach for Black Bike Week, which, just like the loft party, would stay in my memory forever!

Chapter Sixteen

A few weeks before the Myrtle Beach trip, I'd reconnected with Dominic's friend, Santino, which turned out to be something I never saw coming. It was the beginning of May, which just so happened to be prom season around the country. I ran into him on his daughter's prom day while they were out taking pictures downtown.

The last time I saw him was around the time Dominic and I called it quits. Because he was Dominic's friend, I'd kept my distance. But there I was nearly five years later, laying my eyes on him again. I was now twenty-six years old, and I wasn't sure if he would remember me. I circled the block a few times, before our eyes connected. When they did, he stepped away from taking prom photos and walked up to me in my car.

"Kandi? Is that you? What's up, Ma?" he asked.

"Yeah, it's me. In the flesh."

"Damn, it feels like forever since I last saw you. How you been?"

"I'm fine. Same shit this way, just making money and taking care of home. That's it. Good seeing you."

"Word. You still in the entertainment business?"

"You know it. I'm not sure if you heard about it, but I run my own company now. Ya' girl been booked and busy like crazy."

Santino dipped his hands in his pockets and nodded. I had already peeped his wedding ring that was still there. "As a matter of fact, I have heard about it. Kandi's Dazzling Entertainment, right?"

"Yep, that's me."

He laughed and was smiling just as much as I was. "Damn, that's what's up!"

We continued to chat for a while, and before I knew it, we were caught up in a conversation about old times. That's when his daughter interrupted us.

"Daddy," she yelled from behind. "We need you for the pictures!"

I figured she was probably wondering what in the hell we were talking about that was so important, because the two of us went back and forth for a very long time. I didn't mind her halting the conversation, because I wasn't sure where we were headed at the time.

I had a few girls in the car with me, not to mention, I never talked personal business while working, so it was cool.

"Yes, baby," he said to his daughter. "Here I come!"

"I didn't mean to hold you too long," I said. "But it was good to catch up."

"No doubt. Maybe we can link for some drinks one day or something."

I was surprised he had suggested that, but for some reason, thoughts of Dominic were fresh on my mind. "Santino, that would be nice and all, but my kids and business keep me so busy. I rarely have time for myself. I'm sorry."

The smirk on his face implied he wasn't giving up. "Well, I'll book a party then."

I was puzzled, and wasn't sure if he was trying to make his way into my life or not. As hard as I wanted to drive away, I couldn't resist once he started talking my money language. I gave him a business card, hoping he'd use it.

"If that's what you want to do then let's do it. Call me and we'll set it up."

"Sounds like a plan," he said, before walking away.

I had to take another look at his fine ass, and then I drove away. Thoughts of Dominic stayed in my head; it had been years since I'd last seen or heard from him. I just didn't want to go there with Santino, because of his connections with Dominic. I also knew he had a wife who'd been around since way before the first time I'd met him. I wasn't sure what their relationship was like at the time, but I do know that he'd put everything of his in her name.

I also knew his wife had known about me. We never said much to each other, and when Santino called and tried to disrupt my work schedule, I could no longer help myself. I reminded him that he'd had a wife, because his conversations with me started to get more on a personal level. That didn't work for me, and I was blunt about why our phone calls had to cease.

"The truth is I'm busy, you married and you're Dominic's friend. I'm not with any of that, so let's make this the last time we talk. Besides, I have a business to run. I can't get much done, if you keep calling here."

Santino was a smart man. He caught the drift and realized I wasn't fucking with him, until money was on the floor. To get my attention, he called back two days later to book a party.

"Set it up," he said. "I'd like to book you for an event I'm trying to do for my guys."

"What type of event will it be?" I was surprised by the difference in our conversation from a few days ago when I had checked him for beating around the bush.

Another reason why I'd held my guards up was because, during this time, I didn't too much understand the magnitude of the type of man Santino was. It had been a long time since we'd last connected, and I honestly wasn't checking for him. But once we'd made a business connection, I got to see more and more of what he'd been doing. He owned a building in Highland Park, Michigan, a small city on the outskirts of Detroit where he employed numerous younger guys who he decided to throw the party for. Now, like I just said, I wasn't aware of his status in the city, so when he mentioned his guys, I was thinking construction or something. Little did I know, he was one of the biggest heavy hittas in the city at the time. Santino put up every single dime for the party and his friends didn't have to come out of one red cent. He'd gone to the bank to get a slew of ones for the party, just so his friends would have a good time. Shocked that day, I watched him hand out stacks of ones to his friends that totaled, at least, ten thousand dollars. Them niggas were ready!

The event was thrown in a warehouse he owned in Highland Park. It was set up like a huge lounge area with couches and big screen TVs. He'd hired a DJ, so the music was already bumping when we slid in. The open space was full of his men who were ready for my girls. Santino had booked about twenty of them, so they were all thrilled to be there when we arrived and saw what was going on. For one, it wasn't like a strip club where one girl serviced a couple guys at once. I always did my bookings equal as far as ratio, so it wouldn't be unfair moneywise. I made sure the men who booked my parties knew how many guys they thought would be there. That way, attention would be given to everyone. Nobody wanted to be at a party with fifty guys and five girls. My objective was to keep the ratio of men to women at least five-to-two, so even if a girl was off giving a private dance, I still had plenty of girls out on the floor. Whenever there weren't enough women at the party, guys started to get restless. They started fighting over the girls, and then if there were too many girls, and not enough guys, then the girls started fighting over the guys.

When Santino got a chance to sit back and see this twenty-six-year-old boss bitch in boss mode, I think it turned him on more. Not only that, but he was turning me on as well. I liked men who had other niggas catering to them and seemed to be in control. His guys kept coming up to him, referring to him as the "boss." When I'd heard them addressing him like that, I knew he'd come up harder in the world than I'd previously thought. The last time I'd seen him, he was running credit card scams on the side, while running his construction business full time. Now, the game had changed and we were both recognized, and respected, as bosses. Boss or not, the whole time I was at the party I gave him the cold shoulder. He couldn't stomach it not one bit, and he jumped in front of me as I was on my way to see what was up with one of my girls.

"What's up, Ma? Why you ignoring me?" he asked. "You been real short with me tonight, and I don't know why?"

All I said was "no I'm not" and stepped around him to keep it moving. I'd done it because something inside of me wasn't feeling it. I had a rule about dating Dominic's friends and associates. They were close enough that I made an "off limits" rule when it came to Santino. As I'd explained to him before, I was about my money and my kids. That was it. My money was handled, and Monte and I were still co-parenting, so I was never the type to sweat a nigga. He quickly found that out.

Living the life of a boss bitch included me doing what I wanted to do. If I died today, I could say I lived a good life. No relationship regrets, no regrets on nothing. I've had money. I've been broke. I've had hundreds of thousands of dollars. I've probably done touched millions in my lifetime. And I had that clear in mind, even back then at the party with Santino.

It wasn't no secret that he only threw the party to get at me. And to be honest, I struggled with it because I did like the little effort he'd put behind it. I continued to keep my distance from him that night, and I promised him that I'd reach out again whenever I'd had some free time.

The night before Myrtle Beach, Santino gave me a call. We chopped it up long enough for me to know he was trying to see me again. I was leaving in a few hours, so I was super busy riding around collecting money from niggas for parties and for my own personal spending, before I dipped out to Myrtle Beach.

"Do you need any extra money before you leave?" he asked. I had just tucked money in my purse that I'd gotten from a client and was getting back in my car.

"Naw, but I can always use extras," I said.

"Okay. I'll put some money in yo mailbox then. Consider this a down payment."

I pursed my lips and rolled my eyes. "Whatever, nigga. Right. I gotta go and will holla at you when I get back."

I didn't even wait until he'd said goodbye, before ending the conversation. I knew what I was making from parties, but that was business money. I needed personal spending money in my pocket too, so in no way would I turn down his money.

When I got back home, it was almost two in the morning. Just for the hell of it, I checked my mailbox to see if the money was there.

To my surprise, it was. He really did put a couple bands in there with a note that said, *Have a ball on me.* I couldn't help but laugh to myself because I knew he didn't know I was going to Myrtle Beach for a booked event. He thought it was just for a vacation. I instantly reached for my phone to give him a call. I assumed he was waiting, because he answered on the first ring.

"Hey, I got your package," I said. "Thank you, I appreciate it."

"No problem. There's plenty more where that came from, if you just give me the time."

Low key smiling from ear to ear, I could no longer play hard to get. "When I get back, I'll make time!"

Chapter Seventeen

Memorial Day weekend always fell around my birthday, which was also Black Bike Weekend in Myrtle Beach. Roger booked Kandi's Dazzling Entertainment for the Black Bike Week, which in my opinion was too far over the top. But like always, Roger was known for overdoing shit. Businesses like mine weren't necessarily needed at Black Bike Week, especially since there was already going to be a million half-naked girls walking along the strip. It was similar to Freaknik they used to have in Atlanta. Not only was there going to be tons of bitches there, but also hella niggas on bikes with hella money. It was so much tricking . . . and so much other shit going on that this booking wasn't necessary. But Roger paid upfront for ten girls total, and included the party fee, room rental, car rental, gas and whatever other expenses which were necessities for the weekend.

Since my girls and I had other obligations already booked, we left a day after Roger and his friends. They left on Thursday, and sent their bikes down the day prior. Black Bike Week was such a big thing that they had to pay a few extra people to drive their bikes to Myrtle

Beach. But as big as the weekend was, they didn't mind how much it cost to do it.

Me being me, I had events booked left to right. There was no way I was willing to miss out on money during a weekday just to drive to Myrtle Beach when there wasn't even a guarantee that I'd be making as much money as I did back in Detroit. Because of that, we didn't hit the road until early Friday morning. It was after Roger and his boys had already left for the ten-to-twelve-hour drive we'd all had ahead of us.

Upon arrival, the first thing we did was check into our rooms. Dallas had come to Detroit from Alabama to drive down with me, so I roomed with her. All of the girls were hyped as fuck and ready to get the party started. We had sweeping ocean views from our rooms, and were living in true luxury. For a few of the girls traveling with me, this was a huge experience. Some of them had never even been out of town before in their lives. So, they were real anxious to check out the scenery and so was I. The thing was, the minute we was ready to get shit popping, the whole vibe of our entertainment changed within the blink of an eye. Initially, we were paid to entertain at two parties for

Roger on Friday and Saturday night. But we ended up only doing the first night because Roger had brought sand to the beach. Kandi's Dazzling Entertainment was just not needed with all those free women walking around half naked in the streets. All those women were there to have fun and hook up with men. They weren't there on business like we were, so a man could find what he was looking for without having to pull money from his wallet.

It was also different from what we were used to because we actually had to get men to come to the party. That was a task in itself. Most of the partying was done on the outside—on the strip to be exact—and at night, that bitch was jumping with badass naked bitches and rich niggas on bikes. So, what would be the point of partying inside for a fee, when men could get the same shit, maybe even more outdoors, for literally free? To top that off, we weren't just dealing with average Detroit niggas. These niggas came from all over; I'm talking Cali, New York, Atlanta, Florida, Tennessee, Detroit and many more places. To get men we didn't even know to party inside with us was a bit too much for us to handle.

In Detroit, everybody knew who I was. Niggas knew not to get caught playing with me or disrespecting one of my girls. They knew we had security because they could see them all around. They knew I had connections, and trying me in any way would be a big fail. Niggas back home knew it was best to always stay on my good side, because at the end of the day, I would be the one they needed each and every time for their parties. But out of town, that shit was something different—vastly different actually. Out of town niggas didn't know me, didn't care to know me and didn't have an ounce of respect in their body. They didn't give a fuck about anything I had to say or what I meant to this business. By the end of the trip, though, they understood me better. But our first night there was damn near survival of the fittest. I sat my girls down in the hotel room and schooled them on what to expect and how to handle it, because many of those niggas were being mad disrespectful and were grimy as hell.

"Keep your heads up, have fun, and if any of those muthafuckas say something out of line, come see me."

"Not only that," Dallas added. "But we from the D. We don't take no shit and we don't let no niggas make us feel small. Boss Lady is right. Go out there, have a good ass time and watch yo damn back. Don't go nowhere with nobody you don't know, and if a bitch out there brave enough to say some slick shit to you, slap the shit outta her."

We all laughed and high-fived each other. I always knew how to put smiles on my girls faces when plans changed and shit got a little hectic. Some of them weren't used to how disrespectful these niggas were to females, but I had firsthand experience. The more I traveled, the more I got a feel for what kind of niggas lived where. In D.C., them niggas were metrosexual, lowkey hood. In Atlanta, they were just all the way raunchy. D boys always stood up—they will tell you like it is, point blank. They'll curse you out, if you need cursing out. I knew what to expect with them, and that's that! But whenever we went to an event where niggas were all from out of town, and mixed it with women who've never been out of their own city, it was like a powder keg waiting to blow up. Shit you could get away with saying in the D, didn't work the same way in the ATL. People there would pop off and slap the shit out of you in a heartbeat. They didn't sit around talking shit. I'd learned that quickly, and it was the kind of cultural differences that still exist to this day.

As for me, my mouth was, and still is, real slick. If a muthafucka slapped me, I'd slap his ass right back. My girls had that same temperament, and in Detroit, the women had to be as hard as the niggas. That's how we rolled. We were a different breed of women who didn't put up with a lot of shit like some women, and men, did.

For those who didn't know, Black Bike Weekend wasn't about respecting women or being down with empowering women in any way. They were down with passing out fake money—imagine the next day when some of my girls went shopping, only to be turned away from the stores because the dollars they'd gotten were counterfeit! Yes, counterfeit, but how everything unfolded, we never expected the men we engaged with to do no crazy shit like that.

At first, we struggled with getting more people to come to the party. But it turned out to be a complete success because all of Roger's boys knew the party was popping off and they were there in full numbers. Several other dudes came, and they'd had a blast as well. The second night, Roger was just trying to show off, so that party wasn't even a fully planned event. We didn't even bother wasting our time for night two. We also realized there was already too much sand at that beach for us to make any good money. Not only that, but men from the D weren't also going to pull out their knots in front of men from ATL. They didn't know them like that and everybody had concerns about getting robbed. Nobody wanted to be put in a vulnerable position of being closed in a room for a party, but we hadn't thought of that scenario, until we got there. So, as we skipped out on dancing for night two, we decided to just enjoy ourselves in a completely different atmosphere. Roger understood and still paid us. We made our own fun, and I was ready to turn up and spend all the money the men in my life had put in my pockets, before I'd left. Right as I started spending it, and the other girls started spending theirs, that's when they realized some of the money, they had made from dancing was fake. Embarrassed as hell, we went back to the hotel room to figure out what in the hell had happened.

"Aye," Chocolate said while examining money that was spread on the bed. "Y'all see this shit? A lot more of it is fake as hell."

Our mouths were wide open. I was completely distraught as I snatched the bill from her hand. "Let me see this shit. Oh, I know you fucking lying."

Dallas was still in disbelief. "Chocolate, stop playing. That shit ain't counterfeit. A few of it was, maybe, but not all of that."

Chocolate kept examining the money while I kept touching it. "No, for real," she said. "I can't make this shit up and I know fake money when I see and feel it."

A 'what the fuck' look was stuck on all of our faces. We just couldn't believe this shit. Now, I wasn't sure if the fake money came from the party we did or not. A few of the girls went out that night to do some extracurricular activities for more cash. Maybe they got counterfeit money in return for their labor, for all I know. I was mad, but couldn't really do shit about it. We'd never encountered fake money before, so none of us had thought to look for it or to take precautions to avoid getting it. My girls were still mad as hell. They were ready to hurt somebody.

"Fuck this shit," Chocolate said. "I'ma 'bout ready to go snatch some niggas up and beat they asses! What kind of shit is that? What kind of niggas give hard working bitches counterfeit money?"

Chocolate was so mad that she swiped all the money off the bed and watched it hit the floor. Dallas and the others were hot too.

"That shit was foul," Dallas said. "But unfortunately, we don't even know where to find the niggas who gave us that shit. I swear, though, if I see any of the muthafuckas we crossed paths with, y'all gon' have to come get me outta jail."

I couldn't even defend the shit; it was dirty in every way possible. I'd heard of it happening to some other girls a while back, but a nigga in the D wouldn't dare do it. They ass would be embarrassed as hell as soon as it was revealed that it was them. And if it had ever happened at one of my parties, my security would have stomped the fuck out of them. This was a lesson for all of us, but I was determined to put it behind us and cheer my girls up.

The day after that, the trip took a turn for the better. So much so, that I even decided to ride bikes for the first time ever. It was so much fun, and even though I was scared to get on one, I did. I just wasn't into bikes like Dallas was—she loved riding them. She, along with a guy I used to date in Detroit talked me into it, so I hopped on the back of his bike. He ended up dying a few years later, while down south on his bike in a freak accident. After that happened, I probably rode a bike once or twice, but never more, because I was too terrified to do so. My favorite thing about riding bikes was when the bike came to a stop and made my booty bounce. It made my booty look so good, and I played it up the whole time. Plus, I looked real cute on the back of a bike, and held on so tight I almost made a nigga crash! Later that night, DMX and the Ruff Ryders did a bike show that we all got to witness. Our trip was definitely one for the books, and from that moment on, it made me more cautious of out of town niggas and warned me to always check the fucking money before leaving any party.

Chapter Eighteen

Like Santino had said, his giving me money for my trip was his down payment on me, basically putting my ass on layaway. And guess what, I did what the fuck he expected me to do, which was go have a ball on his ass. Nonetheless, I decided to keep my word and give him a little more time. That meant, we eventually started seeing each other more and more. I did so because I understood one thing: money talks and bullshit walks, period. Santino knew the best way to keep me in his presence was to constantly book parties, so he booked more and more parties for no reason at all. It could be a boring ass Friday where everyone was just chilling. Of course I'd show up for him to see me as much as he wanted. We both were busy like crazy during that time, though, and he knew clubbing wasn't my style, unless it was specific clubs like The Legend, The River Rock or any club where I was automatically VIP. I didn't do long lines, and having to wait to get into a club was out of the question. But once we started mingling more and more, he would invite me out to meet him at clubs. A lot of times I would take my girls with me. I didn't even realize how big Kandi's had gotten, until one night we were at a club in downtown Detroit, and when we walked in, the DJ went crazy on the mic, calling us out with crazy shout-outs. His announcements had heads turning from left to right.

"Oh shit, Kandi and her girls are in the muthafuckin' house! Bow down to the queens, niggas, bow the fuck down!"

Everybody was biting our shit, and we just waved like contestants in a beauty pageant and smiled.

"Heeeey," I said, giving dap to people who reached out to me. "What's up?"

Jealousy was in so many bitches' eyes. Only a few had enough courage to step up to me.

"Hey Miss Kandi. Can I join the crew or what?" one chick asked. I didn't play people like some celebs did, and I stopped to give her one of my business cards.

"Call me next week and let's talk."

She took the card and muffled her scream like I was a celebrity. I loved it. I couldn't even lie, even though I didn't too much care about fame. By the time I got to Santino's section, he and his boys were popping bottles like crazy. Popping bottles in the club nowadays shows you got a couple dollars, but back then, it really meant you were a high roller. Now, it's the norm and in order to even get a booth, you have to get a bottle. Back then, you only had to pay an entry fee. Only ballers were popping bottles. Regular niggas just bought a Long Island and sat the fuck down. Now, everybody and they mama got a bottle with hella niggas drinking out of it. It wasn't like that back then. Niggas wasn't spending four-to-five hundred dollars in the club, but that's exactly what Santino and his boys did. He'd had an entourage of, at least, fifteen dudes with him. We turned the fuck up quick with them niggas and had ourselves a ball.

The one thing that attracted me to Santino was the fact that he wasn't stingy. When he was on, he put his entire crew on, and this one specific night it showed. Everybody with him had their own expensive bottle in their hand, their necks were full of gold and silver, and they had wads of cash in their pockets. Some weren't even good looking men, but who really gave a fuck when it came to being around a bunch of rich ass niggas like them? The majority of them had prissy, high maintenance broads with them, but them bitches couldn't fuck with me and my girls. The protocol was to shut shit down for real and we most certainly did. We turned it up in that VIP section, and Santino couldn't keep his hands off me. I don't know how I was able to keep my hands off him, because with his ponytail slicked back, light skin flawless as fuck and bad-boy attire that validated he was the richest nigga in there, I wanted to tear his ass up.

"You know I want you, don't you, Ma?" he said, whispering in my ear as he danced behind me. I could feel his dick poking me—that shit felt real good. "I want you in the worse way, 'cause we make a dope ass couple. You're a boss and so am I."

He was saying all the right words to sway me in his direction. I just kept shaking my ass while teasing the hell out of him. When I finally faced him, I stared into his eyes and wished like hell that all the people around us tossing back alcohol, yelling rap lyrics and partying hard weren't even there.

"All I can say about that is call me. Maybe I'll answer, maybe I won't. That's just a chance you gotta take."

A sly grin appeared on his face. Deep down, he knew I'd had a soft spot for him, and once I started granting him more time, he easily took advantage of it. I low key loved it. He would always go on road trips for business and invite me to tag along for company. His sheltering me never allowed me to see his business side. We would go on trips a day or two before his meetings, hang out, date . . . and do all types of nice things, but the minute it was time to handle business, he would leave me loads of money to go shop or do whatever I wanted to do to stay busy. Me being the fly ass bitch I was, that was more than enough. And the road trips happened frequently. It was good time spent between the two of us. I felt like I had a win-win and nobody could tell me anything different.

***

By the time the Essence Festival rolled around, my homegirl Sinclaire and I decided to roll out for a relaxing vacation that was much needed. She was in nursing school at Wayne State University, while I ran my business 24/7. This trip was something we just couldn't wait for. On top of that, Sinclaire's sorority sister and our mutual friend, Sylvia, planned the entire trip for us. Sin and I decided to drive to New Orleans. We had our schedules all figured out, and couldn't wait to get away. Santino was the nigga I was somewhat pressing at the time, but unfortunately, he wasn't the one I was fucking. A dude named Deon and I was; he was someone I'd known from the hood since I was nine years old. He was the neighborhood fresh kid—Coogi and all. He was about five years older than me, and was the only young dude walking around with Gucci or whatever top name brand clothing you could think of. He never decided to approach me, until I'd gotten older. So, yeah, I was dating Santino, but I was having sexual intercourse with Deon. He had chased me consistently for about seven years, before I decided to give in. It wasn't because I wasn't attracted to him because he was definitely my type. But being from my hood was a big no-no for me. That's too close to home, and sometimes wires get crossed. Old scores come back. Drama kicks up. But, as we all know, there's always that one nigga who slips through the cracks.

In my case, the one who had done so was a real bad boy. He sold drugs and did anything else you could think of to make money. I don't think he ever even had a real job, so during the time we'd dated, he was on tether for drugs for about six months to a year. He would book parties for his boys right in his house, just to spend time with me and have some fun. Because of his situation, he could only leave the house during the day. He was cool as hell, always looked out for me and took care of me as well. I took care of him too, and he would ask me to do little things like go to Red Lobster or pick up something at the store for him, since he couldn't leave. He would give me a thousand dollars just to go do that and tell me to go shopping with the rest. I truly had some good guys in my circle; him and Santino were the best.

The minute both of them found out I was going to New Orleans, they cashed me out instantly, like I knew they would. I partied my life away from the time we arrived to the time we departed. It was much wilder than I expected. Bourbon Street was so crazy that it smelled like nothing but throw up and alcohol from people being so intoxicated. Every major artist you could think of at the time was in the building performing. In addition to celebrities performing, some were walking around as if they were regular people just hanging, slanging and drinking with some of anybody. I'm talking basketball players, actresses and actors . . . whoever else you can think of. I couldn't even believe half of the celebrities we got a chance to link and hang with while we were there. Because one of Sylvia and Sin's sorority sisters worked at the concert, we were able to get backstage passes at every single event held that weekend. Not only were the celebrities cool, everyone else was as well. Well, most people were, and I quickly learned that my slick mouth could get me in trouble. Everybody knows I will curse a nigga out in a heartbeat . . . except in New Orleans. Voodoo is real, and at the time, New Orleans was known for it. I didn't need that voodoo shit coming down on me. But, I noticed that New Orleans only had people dark like me or people who were high yella Creoles. That freaked me out, because there was a whole group of people I just didn't see there. No brown people. No caramel people. Just dark and yella.

With that being said, I'd met a Creole guy the very last night I was there. He was handsome, yella, and had some real beautiful blue eyes. Only thing, he was crazy as hell too! I'd only known him for one night—and we didn't even have sex—yet he was all in my ear talking crazy while we sat at a restaurant eating.

"I'll move to Detroit, get a job up there and take real good care of you," he said. He was a fast talker too. "Can I do that for you? Huh? Huh?"

Thirsty niggas irritated the hell out of me, and I felt the same way about ones who were so open and willing to risk it all. I quickly shut down his plans and was ready to move on to bigger and better things that night.

"Uh, nigga no. That won't work for me."

He kept pressing. "Why not? Don't you want me to take care of you and live—"

"Hell, no. Now, move back and give me some breathing room. Damn!"

I was so frustrated that I'd got up from the table and left. I straight up thought he was going to do some voodoo shit on me, and even though I'd had a grand time for the duration of my trip, I kept watching my back and being extra careful just in case he was into some type of witchcraft.

On the drive home, Sin and I discussed how much fun we had. We were two young girls just living our lives and enjoying our freedom. If I could do that shit all over again, I most certainly would. I was on cloud nine, but then my mind shifted to my menstrual cycle. I would always time my cycles with whatever it was I had going on, so if I thought I would be on my cycle while on a trip, I wouldn't go. Or, I would plan it to where I would be heading home the day it started. But this particular time, shit just wasn't right and my smarty pants ass was so far wrong. I knew I should have been on my cycle, but because I had gotten so fucked up the night before, I was sick as a dog. I blamed the delay of my cycle on the liquor.

"Bitch, you sure you not pregnant?" Sin asked while side-eying me.

"Hell naw." I was crouched over while holding my stomach.

"Kandi, yo ass don't know for sure. I'm about to pull over and get you a pregnancy test because this yo tenth time throwing up within the past three hours."

Me being me, the smart bitch, of course, I knew a positive test was never wrong. Now a negative test, maybe, but a positive one, hell naw. So my only goal was to make sure that bitch didn't end up positive. I was praying my ass off while sweating at the same time as we rushed into the store and purchased a pregnancy test. I hurried into the bathroom, slamming the stall behind me. Once the door was locked, I yanked down my pants and held the pregnancy test between

my legs. I was so nervous that my legs were trembling.

"You alright in there girl," Sin yelled. "What it say?"

"Nothing yet, but gimmie a minute. I'm okay."

Minutes later, I wasn't okay. I damn near broke down after

seeing the positive symbol, and all Sin could do was hug me.

"Girl, it's gon' be okay. We got you and you ain't got to worry

about nothing."

I knew my girls had me, but what she didn't know was I had a

lot to worry about. I cried the entire ride home just thinking about it. I

couldn't believe this shit, and I kept gazing out of the window

thinking, "Hell naw. This can't be!" I was just in that much disbelief.

The minute I got home, Santino called me to link up with him.

We met later that night at Hot Tamale Gentlemen's Club to hang and

do some catching up, while being entertained by strippers who danced

in front of us. We were sitting at the bar, going shot for shot. My crazy

ass, still in denial about my pregnancy, decided to drink my problems

away. By the time our night came to an end, I was plastered yet again.

But in the middle of all the drinking, I'd also decided that night would be the night I would have sex with Santino. The flirting had lingered on for years, and even though we were back in each other's lives, we hadn't slept together. We never took it there, and with all that liquor in me and trouble on my mind, I was ready for that night to be the night we changed all that.

Santino and his entourage were having a ball with the other bitches his niggas brought with them. I sat there with my pregnancy weighing heavily on my mind, and if I could do anything to divert my attention elsewhere, I would. The drinking helped, and right as the club was about to close, Santino approached me about the next move for the night.

"Look, I'm about to ghost all these people," he said. "Go around the corner and wait on me."

Right at that moment, the DJ had wrapped up the last song. Santino telling me that was his way of getting rid of his entourage so he could be with me for the night. I was cool with it, so around the corner I went. At the time, I was driving a Blazer truck. I could barely drive—I was so drunk, but I managed to park in a spot on the road that had a good view of the parking lot of the club, so I could see him when he came out. I sat there for about five minutes, thinking about my situation and so fucked up from the alcohol. A few minutes later, I removed my keys from the ignition and turned the truck off. People started coming out of the club, talking loud as their voices filled the air. I watched numerous people walk to their cars while trying to figure out what else to get into for the remainder of the night. Santino was nowhere in sight, so I lowered my head on the steering wheel and yawned. My eyelids got heavier and heavier, so I closed my eyes and escaped into darkness.

By the time I woke up, I realized my goofy ass had fallen asleep while waiting on his slow ass. With no keys in the ignition, in the middle of the road, I didn't wake up until five a.m. The sun was just beginning to rise and was beaming inside of my car. I squinted, before realizing I had slept away my fucking opportunity with him and not in a good way! It was grace and mercy that didn't nobody knock me in the head, rob me or take my truck, because my truck was literally parked in the middle of the street, in DETROIT, where niggas were always ready to rob somebody for a come up.

DETROIT MADAM

After I got myself together, the first thing I did was search for my phone. I just knew Santino had been blowing my shit up. Sure enough, I was right. He had called about twenty times, and going for what he suspected in the texts he'd sent me, he thought I was out doing some crazy shit. The whole time, I was a block over in the middle of the street slumped. I shook my head and drove home. The minute I got home, and got comfy in my bed, my phone started ringing nonstop from an unknown number. It turned out to be his woman—but not his wife who I already knew about. It was his side bitch calling my phone—a bitch I'd never even heard of before.

"You fucking with my nigga! Where that nigga at? I see he called you like twenty times, so I know he there wit' you!"

At first, I was so confused because I didn't know who this was yelling in my ear so early in the morning. Two, how did she even get my number? And three, how did she even see my number on *his* phone? The more she talked, the quicker I understood who she was and how her retarded ass was able to see his calls from her phone bill account. Keep in mind that I was already pissed, because as much as I wanted Santino, it had come to this. I had been waiting for the right opportunity for us to hook up, since we'd reconnected. In all actuality, more like seven years. Thinking about that, while listening to her foolishness had me hot. I slowly sat up in bed to get my bearings, and started cussing her ass out.

"Listen, you raggedy bitch, he wasn't with me. But the nigga was supposed to be, and please believe if he was, we wouldn't be answering the phone right now to talk to yo dumb ass. Instead, I'd be fucking the shit outta him, before sending him back to his wife, not you. So get the fuck off my phone and go find something productive to do with yo time, instead of calling other bitches looking for a nigga who obviously don't want you."

"Really bitch," was all she could say. That's normally what a bitch would say, whenever she got checked. I continued to go off on her ass. She should've known better calling me and interrupting my fucking sleep.

"You know his ass ain't over here, and obviously I didn't answer my phone if he had to call me twenty fucking times! Stop being so stupid, and don't you ever, in yo entire fucked-up lifetime, call my muthafucking phone again."

CLICK!

I dismissed that bitch and immediately called his phone. He answered right away.

"Yo bitch just called me, and you know I don't play that shit. A nigga like you should have better control of your shit, and you know damn well I don't have time for stupid hoes to be calling my phone."

"Calm down, au'ight? I apologize for her and the situation already being handled. But where in the fuck was you—"

I was so mad that I barely gave him a chance to talk. I knew he was mad about the night before, but once she called, I no longer cared about that anymore.

"Nigga, I was just on the next block over passed the fuck out drunk waiting on yo ass. You took too damn long! But about yo bitch calling me, though! You already know the rules. Don't have no bitch calling my phone cuz I ain't lyin' for no nigga. First thing I'm gon' encourage her to do is talk to her muthafucking nigga, instead of me. If she than already reached out to yo ass and still got issues, then I'ma tell that bitch some shit she don't wanna hear. So get yo house in order, and just so we're clear on the record, if I fuck you, I'm telling."

Santino didn't give a fuck. He laughed at the shit and kept trying to apologize on her behalf. I honestly didn't give a damn either, so as he was talking, I hung up on him and went back to sleep. I wasn't sure if it was all the cussing I'd done, or the liquor, but I was sick for the next three days straight. It was to the point where I couldn't eat or drink anything. I was throwing up and couldn't hold nothing down. After the third day of going through hell, I had to go to the hospital. That's when I found out I was having twins. Not one baby, but two. I looked at the nurse with tears at the rims of my eyes, ready to pour over.

"Twins?" I repeated. "Are you sure? How can you tell?"

"By looking at the ultrasound," she said, trying to console me. "I also hear two heartbeats, but try to relax. I see that the news is shocking to you. If you'd like to speak to someone about how you're feeling about this, please let me know."

Talk about hurt, a bitch was hurt. Don't get me wrong, I love my twins with every bone in my body. But that was just something I was not ready for. I felt like I was losing my damn mind, and there was no way to come back to my senses.

"Fuck!" I screamed and shouted in the solitary confinements of my own bedroom. I started tearing up shit; it was the only way I could express what I was feeling inside. "Damn, damn, damn!" I ripped the sheets, pulled down the curtains and broke my lamp when I pitched it against the wall. Shards of glass scattered everywhere, and when I saw so many pieces of glass, I fell back on my bed, crying my heart out. My fists were tightened and I kept pounding them on the mattress. "I hate I gotta call this nigga and tell him," I mumbled and bit into my bottom lip. I just couldn't believe this was my life; I wasn't ready to accept that I was pregnant, let alone having twins. Regardless, Deon needed to know. I had to call and tell him. Twins ran in both of our families—my brother has a set of twins and my sister had lost a set. I guess it shouldn't have been a shock, but it didn't dawn on me when I had gotten the news.

All I could do was process the news the best way I knew how. It wasn't bad when you went from two to three kids, but when you go from two to four? That's doubling the amount of kids you have all at once! I kept asking myself how the hell I was going to do this and make it work. Somehow or someway, I had to do it.

Now, I always considered myself a realistic person. If you screw without a condom, there's a possibility you might get pregnant. I couldn't be mad at nobody but myself. I couldn't be mad at Deon. I couldn't be mad at God. The only person I could be mad at was me, because if I didn't want to get pregnant, I should have taken precautions. Eventually, that's how I coaxed myself into looking at my life. I was accountable for my actions, and reality was starting to set in.

Once I'd made a decision to tell Deon, I thought about Santino too. I'd been telling him that I hadn't been talking to nobody else, other than him. I even went as far to say I wasn't fucking anyone at the time. If that was the case, then how in the hell could I come up pregnant? Because Santino been so close to me, I had some explaining to do. He wasn't aware of my motto, "I only screw one guy at a time, but I always have another nigga prepped." That's just how it was. I was sleeping with Deon, prepping Santino and got caught up.

Because Deon was the only nigga I'd been fucking, I knew my babies were his, so I called to tell him. He was like, "Whatever you wanna do is fine with me. I'll fly wit' it."

He already had two girls, but he never asked me to get an abortion. But that was it and he didn't say much more. By the time winter rolled around, and since Monte had still been coming around to see the kids, I hooked back up with him. He was super excited about my twins, because he himself was a twin. He couldn't wait until the twins arrived.

To avoid having this conversation with Santino, I just disappeared on him, until well after the twins were born. I did it so smooth that he assumed I stopped talking to him because his bitch had called me. That wasn't even the case. I was sick behind my decision, because no matter how much I didn't want to like Santino, I just couldn't get him off my mind. It bothered the fuck out of me for a long time.

But as usual, Monte was like my savior. He was there for me, and I've never had to be pregnant by myself. He'd stepped up to the plate for my kids, when their fathers hadn't. So, at the end of the day, Monte came to the rescue for this spoiled brat right here.

"One day," he said, holding me in his arms. My emotions were running high, and it felt good to have him comforting me. "It's just gon' be you, me and the kids. Nobody else and all of this hurt you feeling inside will be washed away."

I smacked my tears away and looked up at him. We had been through so much, and there he was still standing with me through it all.

"Thank you," I said. "Thank you for everything and I'll never forget how good you've been to me."

We both were determined to raise a family together one day. Those were always my intentions, which was why we ended up back together.

We were together, but not without incident. Monte's drinking always did something to fuck up the plans we'd made. Sometimes, he'd stop drinking for a minute; he even went to AA. But then something would always happen to bring him right back to square one with the bottle.

As I got bigger and bigger with the twins, and their birth got closer and closer, Monte's excitement rubbed off on me. After I'd had my first daughter, Monte and I had tried to get pregnant, but it never happened. So, this time leading up to me giving birth to the twins, enabled us to relive those moments again in some ways. Honestly, I think it was God who made sure Monte and I never had a child together. However, he did have a biological child when he'd gotten married to someone else later. If we'd had one together, it would have been a "til death do us part," situation. We just could never make it work long enough for that to be realistic.

At the same time, the pregnancy forced me to slow back down. It reintroduced money issues into my life, and I'd stopped doing parties for a minute. No one really knew why I'd stopped. I just stopped, and since I was a private person who didn't put my business out there, no one really questioned it. My life had taken on a slower pace. I'd gone from doing something every single day of the week— being up until all hours of the night—to being more focused on my kids.

The only thing that kept my mind busy during my pregnancy was work, so that's what I did. I continued to book parties for other girls, but had no choice but to slow up my appearances. There was a time that I only arrived at events to collect money and provide clients with receipts. I was just too tired and out of it. My girls and security covered everything, because at that point, we had been in business so long that they knew what to do without me in some regards. Nevertheless, this was one summer that I couldn't do nothing I wanted to do or had planned.

Deon's mama had stepped in to help out too. She caught the slack of her son who was still out in the streets. Our twins gave her her first grandson, who is a "junior." Because of that, she was very attached to them. She bought their cribs, along with so many other things they needed at the time. She, herself, had a set of twins, and she also had twin brothers. There were just twins every damn where! I was ready for the changes they would bring to my life, but I didn't know if those changes would happen fast.

Chapter Nineteen

Right after I'd had the twins, things were on and popping again. I was back with the shits. Summertime hit and me and the gang was back throwing parties, ass shaking, and money making again. I was living my best life as a mama of four, and right in the midst of it all, I crossed paths with Santino yet again. Bitch was clean that day; then again, so was he.

"Damn, Ma," he said, checking me out as I was leaving a restaurant with one of my clients. "You just fell off the face of the earth."

"Yeah, nigga, I did. You know me well enough to know drama is something I don't do."

"You know I'd never put yo fine ass into no type of drama. I mean that shit." He paused to lick his lips and gazed at me for a few seconds. "Anyway, what's been up?"

I shrugged and tried to play down my enthusiasm. "Just doing the normal working during the day and doing parties at night. What about you?"

"Same shit, different day. Still doing me, but you know you ain't got to be out here doing what you doing, if you was riding with me. I'm just putting that out there, but it's up to you."

"I hear you talking, but let me give it some thought. I'll let you know what's up."

I walked away with some heavy things on my mind. This go around, shit was different with the parties. Times had changed, and they just weren't a hot commodity like they were before. Girls had started messing up the game and were doing parties for free. Basically, doing shit for McDonald's money, so niggas had gotten used to that and didn't want to pay for girls at parties anymore. I witnessed the decline firsthand and realized it just wasn't lucrative for me anymore. I'd been out of the game for a year at that point and other girls had come in and tried to do what I was doing. But it never popped off for them, the way it did for me. They didn't know how to run a business the way I did. They didn't know the game like I did. A lot of girls had retreated back into the strip clubs and started back making money that way since I'd been gone. It all just fizzled out. It was the start of it all dying down, and for me . . . it wasn't fun anymore.

I was twenty-seven, almost twenty-eight, and I had to start thinking about other things. I now had four kids—nine years old, three years old and one-year-old twins. I had never thought about this line of work as my life's work, my legacy. I'd created a nice lifestyle for myself, but I'd never meant for this to be a permanent gig in the first place. Now, life couldn't just be all about fun. I had to grow up. I had to face the times. I had to find a new way to make money and build myself into being the woman I always knew I wanted to be.

Right around the time I'd run into Santino again, Monte and I decided to split ways for good this time. After two years of trying to make it work for the second time around, it was just time to let go.

DETROIT MADAM

Monte would have been the perfect man for me, honestly. But liquor had a way of bringing out certain sides of people that most people like me could never deal with. Monte was the definition of a true alcoholic who made too many excuses and couldn't stay on track for nothing. It hurt me like hell to walk away from him, and when I did, a few months later, I started kicking it with Santino. I couldn't even explain why, but it was just something about this nigga that I couldn't shake. During the two years I'd ghosted from his life, he had elevated again like crazy. I wasn't talking no little weed-like shit. I'm talking big-time cartel shit. Santino was making so much money that he was finding any and every reason to throw a party and celebrate. The Super Bowl was even enough for him to throw the most expensive party of the year. It was so extravagant, and it seemed like everybody who lived in Detroit was there. There were about forty girls and hella niggas that were some of the top drug lords in the city. But, like always, all good things come to an end. That's what happened to Santino, shortly after that last party with him.

People began to snitch on him, money began to dry up, plugs began to ghost, indictments . . . all types of shit happened. Literally, everything that could possibly go wrong for Santino did, and when the heat turned up, things between us were on shaky ground. Six months after the Super Bowl party, his life changed forever. He was a smart man, and he knew the feds were closing in on him. He felt them watching him. And he was pretty sure it had all stemmed from a nigga who'd owed him money a while back. The nigga messed around and got kidnapped, fucking with Santino. Only, it turned out that the guy who got kidnapped was an informant. They tortured his ass for the money he'd owed, and when they released him, he went to the feds and squealed like a pig.

Now, Santino wasn't there when the kidnap and torture happened, but the informant said he'd ordered it. That's what put him on the feds' radar. Santino couldn't do shit about it, and even if he'd wanted to clean up his act, they'd already seen enough to start watching him. With so many eyes on him, he started to get his affairs in order. The case they were trying to build against him was massive, but no matter what happened, he wasn't prepared to snitch. He wasn't that type of nigga, and if he went down, he would go on his own.

DETROIT MADAM

In the meantime, Santino owned a home in Southfield where he threw his sickly mama a birthday party. It was one of the most elegant events I'd ever been to. Not only was I there, but Santino's wife was there too. I had no choice but to play shit cool. In all honesty, I was only there for a short period of time to deliver my gift and bounce, which I did. A week later, the two of us were together when he'd gotten a call that the same home he owned in Southfield, where he'd had his mama's birthday party, had been robbed. Or, that's what he thought.

"Man, don't no nigga take shit from me!" he shouted into the phone while talking to one of his boys. "We need to find out who those muthafuckas were and deal wit' that shit. That's my damn house, nigga. It's where I draw the fuckin' line!"

He was mad as hell. His whole face was fire red; I had never witnessed him so angry. I figured it would be just a matter of time before he found out who those niggas were. But as we sat there that day and started pondering what had happened, the whole details of the incident made the two of us easily connect the dots. Not only was his house robbed, but it was robbed as if the intruders were looking for something. They'd cut up the couch cushions, and had even tore out the ceilings to remove every camera around the house, so no one could go back and review the tape for evidence, especially, if it was an unlawful search. He had a shed in the back of the house; they damn near tore it down, looking for something. Even his clothes and fur coats had been cut up. The whole damn house was a mess.

We thought it might've been some bad DEA, because they tricked his mama into believing that they were the police and needed to get into the house. They didn't even leave any warrant paperwork behind, so whoever had done it, they'd done it exactly how the feds would do in a raid. This right there sealed the deal for us. Six months later they came down with the actual indictment, which ended up giving Santino two years to get his act together. It took them two years to build the case, but he took the news calmly.

From that point on, it was strictly business for him. He was trying to prepare for his time away with hopes of making sure his family would be good and able to sustain in his absence. He focused on the clean money coming from his legit businesses and socked it away. I understood his grind to make sure his family would be taken care of, so the two of us rarely got a chance to link as much as we had.

Several months later, and with his back against the wall, he took a plea deal. The feds threatened his wife; they threatened to go after her and told him that if he took the plea deal, they would spare her. That, of course, turned out to be a lie. He didn't know that at the time, but instead of giving him the eight years they'd promised, they sentenced him to fifteen to twenty years behind bars. Everything they'd told him about the plea deal, the feds didn't honor any of it. Instead, they said that because of his history, it took his charge up to a level two. He ended up doing thirteen years, and the only reason his sentence got reduced was because of changes in laws that reduced sentencing for drugs.

While he was away, the feds came back and charged his wife with tax evasion. Even though they'd said they wouldn't touch her, if he took the plea deal, she ended up serving time too. She rode with him till the end, but my belief was, "I'ma ride or die, but I ain't ride or die for nobody." When Santino went down, he wanted me to do ride-or-die shit like help him run his businesses, pick up and drop off shit . .

. come visit him and so much more. But I'll tell a nigga in a minute, that's not the lifestyle I wanna live. Now, if that's how you choose to make a living, then do you. No judgement here, do your thing! Me and him had talked several times about him stopping, about us running away together, and him getting out of the game. I tried to tell him, before it had even gotten to that point. But he never stopped. He couldn't stop, he wouldn't stop and he was in too deep.

"You don't understand that I got too many mouths to feed," he said, during one of our conversations. "Niggas depending on me to keep this shit moving. I can't just up and quit. What the fuck I look like?"

His face was all twisted, and I could tell he was insulted by our discussion. But I saw things that he didn't. I had also experienced it in my business, and some of those people he was so concerned about were using the hell out of him. I didn't hold back on saying it.

"They may be depending on you, but they not about to help you, if you go down. I can promise you that, but you gotta learn that on yo own."

He blew that shit off and just wouldn't stop. So, I felt like, basically, he wanted me to ride or die for him riding-or-dying for other muthafuckas. Hell no. I got kids, and I refused to do anything that would send me to jail too.

I did, however, go to the courthouse when he was sentenced. There were a slew of bitches there crying their hearts out, showing how frustrated they were with the judicial system and willing to have his back. I wasn't trying to be just one of a bunch of bitches taking care of this nigga while he was locked away. Nah, that wasn't how I moved, so I left that day and carried the fuck on with my life.

It seemed like the minute Santino was sent away to do fed time, it was a mass hit out on the city. The shit was far beyond me. People were getting knocked off left to right by hittas or got caught up by the feds. Literally, anything you can think of to go wrong at that time did. When I say grace and mercy was on my side, that's exactly what I mean. I don't think my girls and I realized the caliber of dangerous ass niggas we had been fucking with, dancing for, and taking money from. We didn't realize that we were doing business with the infamous BMF. We didn't realize that these niggas throwing parties were the real faces behind some of the biggest drug deals and retaliation murders in the streets. At the time that we'd met them, a lot of them were still up and coming but became made men as we were dealing with them. As is always the case, the big niggas in the game, when I first started in the business, were eventually knocked off. The niggas I'd been throwing parties for were the ones who came up and took their places. Maybe they were even the ones who knocked the first niggas off in the first place. They took over the OGs' streets, made their own mark, all while booking Kandi's Dazzling Entertainment. No matter how they did it, I'm forever grateful to them for putting cash in my girls' thongs, food on their tables, allowing them to further education . . . whatever. The stuff I wasn't happy about was the girls who got caught up in the dope game during the process. That shit bothered me, but we were so caught up with these heavy hittas who'd made it big, ruled the city, and skyrocketed to new levels.

The drought that ran through the city after Santino's sentencing lasted for a while. It was the change of an era, a matter of timing. Nobody knew who was telling on who, but on my end, there weren't as many people trying to book parties. I felt that shit coming to an end, and didn't know how I truly felt about it. That was until I went to a party that let me know it was time to wash my hands and exit the game.

The event was booked through one of my girls. Now, to know me is to know that if I don't know you, I don't work with you. But after my twins, I became more lenient with my business and started letting my girls and security assist more when I couldn't. This just so happened to be one of those times. My girl took over, and it was her people who'd set up the party. At first sight, I walked in impressed. The whole set up was dope and my girls had made a couple of dollars. It wasn't until I stepped into another room, when I realized how problematic shit was. Cocaine was all over the tables, and I walked past men snorting it up, while waving my girls over to do the same. They all said no, and even though I was beyond sick from seeing all of the drugs, I tried to remain calm until it was time to get the fuck out of there. This let me know how much the game had really and truly changed. The parties didn't look the same anymore. It wasn't just about a turn up or a night of sexual fantasies. It had now become more and more about drugs, and no matter how much I tried, I wasn't comfortable with that.

Every single party we'd had, I always made it my business to locate my girls and keep an eye on them. And the minute I noticed girls missing, I went on the hunt for them. Diamond was one of the girls missing that night. I searched high and low for my girl, because she just wasn't on payroll by me, she was one of my bitches, so I needed to know her whereabouts at all times to make sure she was okay. She had been dancing for my company for a while, and was practically one of our day ones who was far removed from her old life as a NFL player's wife. I pushed through the crowded ass party, looking angry and frustrated as hell. My other girls had their hands in the air, shaking their asses and trying to get as much money as they could while bending over in men's faces. Cigarette smoke was thick, and so many rowdy ass niggas were bumping and grinding to the loud music. The minute I got to the small bathroom in the back, I pushed on the door. It swung open, and that's when I saw, for the first time in my entire life, someone snorting coke out of the infamous folded dollar bill. Unfortunately, it was Diamond. Seeing her do that shit was like a gut punch to my stomach. I was instantly sick and snatched her up so quickly that I had to catch myself.

"What the fuck is going on in this bathroom?"

She was out of it. Jumpy and shit and couldn't even string one sentence together to explain herself.

"Look, gurrrl, I just, we—"

I'd never seen this side of the girls, but there was my Foxy Brown looking diva as head of the coke girl pack. Several other girls were in the bathroom with her. I scolded every last one of them.

"If y'all bitches don't get the fuck outta here right now, I'ma start fucking up everybody! Put that shit down and move!"

I was heated, and one by one, I watched each of them walk out of there at a slow pace with long faces. Diamond stayed behind, trying to apologize.

"I—I don't know what done got into me," she said. "I swear it ain't—I won't do this again, and you gotta—"

The way she was talking and seeing her like that just broke my fucking heart in half. More than anything, she was my friend. And not only was she doing that shit, but seeing those other girls waiting to get their hit was a hard ass pill to swallow. The images still haunt me because she was so strung out. Some nigga had pimped her, married her, had her living big, and then introduced her to the cocaine life. I imagined her snorting it off the fucking tables at her house. I imagined my bitch relapsing into those old ways I thought she'd left behind. I couldn't believe that shit. She kept insisting that it was her very first time doing it again.

"I swear I been clean for a long time," she said, while still trying to convince me that she had stopped.

"Ain't no way it's yo first time doing it again, especially if you using that dollar bill! How you know how to do that shit? Your a pro, and I know what I saw with my own eyes!"

I pulled her out the bathroom and made her tell me who there was in on it with her. And, of course, she told on *everybody*. She mentioned who had been snorting with her, when and where. I was DONE. I marched right out there and let those Tony Montana wanna-be niggas have it. By then, niggas was snorting cocaine everywhere I turned.

"Y'all need to put that shit up right now or we out," I said forcefully to the head nigga in charge who was sitting his midnight black ass on a sofa with no shirt on. His six-pack was ripped, while two girls were hanging all over him. I ordered them to get up. "We don't do this shit, boo! Y'all niggas tripping."

Every last one of them niggas looked at me like I was crazy. The ringleader had a smirk on his face, and to let me know my words didn't mean shit, he leaned forward and snorted a mountain of white powder that was on the table.

"Ahhhh," he said, sucking in a deep breath as the other niggas laughed.

His actions were too disrespectful and shit hit the fan quick. Unbeknownst to me, cocaine had become the new marijuana. I was used to weed, but this coke shit was taking it too far for me. When people got on coke, they started wilding out, stealing shit, backstabbing friends, killing people . . . that wasn't the lifestyle I wanted to be around.

Besides that, too many people had been indicted, and with everyone around me going down, there was no way for me to know if *I* was being watched, if one of these niggas at the party was being watched . . . hell, maybe we all were. There was just too much on the line now, and as I stood right there in the middle of that party, I thought about my kids. Everybody always say what they ain't gonna do, and who they not gonna tell, but, at the end of the day, when it came down to me and my family, versus everyone else, I knew who the priority was. Too many mouths flapped, and I couldn't keep being caught up in no bullshit like this.

That day, all I could think of was what career I could find that would take me out of these types of parties and lead me into the next phase of my life. This was fun, but what was next? I'd partied my ass off, but what had it come to now? How would I continue to support my kids outside of all this escalating craziness around me—craziness I'd been living in for a decade nonstop. I realized that I'd had that moment in life and it had passed. I was ready to be grown now.

As I gathered my girls to leave, I noticed those niggas constantly whispering in each other's ears. My intuition was on overload and the whole situation didn't sit right with me. I knew it was time for us to get the hell out of there fast.

"Don't leave nothing behind in this bitch 'cause we ain't coming back," I yelled as my girls were gathering their things. I had my security go out first, so by the time we were ready to make our exit, they were already in cars waiting on us. This was also my way of camouflaging my security in case those niggas tried any slick mess on us. Unfortunately, they did. The minute my security got to their cars, they noticed some of the same guys from inside waiting on us to make our exit, getting closer. That's when my head of security, my brother, who was still a part of the DPD, approached the guys. He had a grip on his Glock and was ready for anything.

"Y'all niggas looking for somebody?" he asked, catching them off guard. They looked at his Glock, saw how buffed he was and had a change of heart.

"Naw," one nigga said. "I lost my watch earlier and they just came out here to help me find it."

"Well, go look in another muthafuckin' direction. It ain't over here, 'cause I already looked."

They quickly backed down, but kept side-eyeing me, before they headed back into the warehouse. From the looks of shit, and from what my gut had told me, I believed that one of the girls in my camp was in on the shit. Had it been a set up to rob me? To hurt me? To scare me? That right there made me feel like I couldn't trust a soul, and I was so far over it from that moment on. I couldn't find the strength to get back into the game, no matter how much I wanted to convince myself. I wasn't putting my life on the line for nobody. Everyone around me wanted me to take the show on the road, but the minute I felt as if my livelihood was in danger, was the minute I knew this business and line of work was no longer for me. That night alone, I'd seen one of my main bitches Diamond snort coke, while another one possibly joined in on an attempted robbery. The signs were all there, and in an effort to show respect to my girls who still respected me, appreciated all that I'd done for them, and even struggled with trying to stay on the right path, I invited them to a meeting to air all of this shit out.

"Is this what y'all do on a regular basis?" I asked as we sat around in my living room talking. "So, cocaine is the new thing, and y'all done let these niggas push that shit on y'all?"

Some implied no, while many others sat silent. If one of them OD'd at one of my events, I would have to answer a whole bunch of questions about what the hell had been going on under my nose. My shit was legal! I didn't need that shit, and as more girls spoke up, that's when I became aware of the serious drugs involved in my company, in their lives and right under my nose. I was never afraid of going to jail for *my fuckups*, but when it came to other people's issues and vices, no way. I didn't have no control over that. I could tell them all day not to do drugs, but if that's the vice they needed to be able to do this—to be able to perform—then they were going to do it on their own.

Looking at it from another perspective, I guess it was just like when I started dancing and had to drink, in order to get loose. That was my choice and I had control over it. But not being able to have control over this situation brought the whole damn house down. It was over, and all I could do going forward was remind my girls that they needed to be more aware of what the fuck they were doing and how they were conducting themselves.

"It's official. I'm done. I want to thank y'all for taking this journey with me, and trust me when I say I've had a lot of fun. But it's time for me to walk. I gotta open some new doors, because the path I saw the other day ain't the path I wanna take. But that's my decision. Y'all gotta make yours. Remember that people gon' always judge you and do whatever to try and bring you down. But be smart and treat yourself good. That's what matters, and wherever you bitches go from here, just know that I love y'all and wish every last one of you bad ass bitches the very best."

We all laughed, hugged and cried that day. It was a day that I'll never forget, but there was no turning back for me. I'd learned a wealth of knowledge from being the Detroit Madam, and I still have so many secrets that I'll take to my grave. But the one thing that I always knew was, it's not how you start in anything you do. It's how you finish, and while I have no regrets about how I chose to live my life, I'm still in the process of finishing this shit in a way that'll make me even prouder of myself.

Since I was used to good money, I continued to attend a few parties here and there, but it wasn't much. Right before Santino was sentenced, I stumbled upon a young guy who was well off into mortgages. I also had a cousin who had been in real estate for years; it was going well for her. That's the route I decided to go. I would always see her make great money doing real estate, but never had enough time to let her teach me the trade. The real estate industry was like the entertainment industry in my eyes—they're both run by men. I knew real estate was something I'd need to invest my time into, and my goal was to find a career that made the same amount of money I'd been making, if not more and with less risks than in the entertainment world. So, once I started watching her more and learning from the guy in mortgages, I knew this was it. I quickly gravitated towards one guy who took the time to show me the ropes, and I can honestly say he helped me become the beast I soon came to be. This guy, like me, was nothing short of a genius. He'd taught me everything from A to Z about mortgages, and I made my transition from the Detroit Madam to the Detroit Broker—a boss lady forever and just like that the next journey started!

Made in the USA
Columbia, SC
01 May 2021

36672306R00163